Student Note-Taking

An Introduction to
Community
Fifth Edition
Health

James F. McKenzie • Rober **cki**

JONES AND BARTLETT PUBLISHERS
Sudbury, Massachusetts
BOSTON   TORONTO   LONDON   SINGAPORE

World Headquarters
Jones and Bartlett Publishers
40 Tall Pine Drive
Sudbury, MA 01776
978-443-5000
info@jbpub.com
www.jbpub.com

Jones and Bartlett Publishers Canada
2406 Nikanna Road
Mississauga, ON L5C 2W6
CANADA

Jones and Bartlett Publishers International
Barb House, Barb Mews
London W6 7PA
UK

ISBN: 0-7637-3485-3

Printed in the United States of America
08 07 06 05 04   10 9 8 7 6 5 4 3 2 1

Contents

How This Book Can Help You Learn

All of us have different learning styles. Some of us are visual learners, some auditory, some learn better by doing an activity. Some students prefer to learn new material using visual aids. Some learn material better when they hear it in a lecture; others learn it better by reading it. Cognitive research shows that no matter what your learning style, you will learn more if you are actively engaged in the learning process.

The *Student Note-Taking Guide* will help you learn by providing a structure to your notes and letting you utilize all of the learning techniques mentioned above. Students don't need to copy every word their professor says or recopy their entire textbook. Do the assigned reading, listen in lecture, follow the key points your instructor makes, and write down meaningful notes. After reading the text and listening to lectures, review your notes and pull out the most important points.

This *Guide* is a great learning tool that follows the chapter topics presented in your textbook, *An Introduction to Community Health, Fifth Edition.* If your instructor is using the PowerPoint slides that accompany the text, this guide will save you from having to write down everything that is on the slides. There is space provided for you to jot down the terms and concepts that you feel are most important to each lecture. By working with this guide, you are seeing, hearing, writing, and, later, reading and reviewing. The more often you are exposed to the material, the better you will learn and understand it. Using different methods of exposure significantly increases your comprehension.

This is the perfect place to write down questions that you want to ask your professor later, interesting ideas that you want to discuss with your study group, or reminders to yourself to go back and study a particular concept again to make sure that you really got it.

Having organized notes is essential when studying for an exam, or when doing homework assignments. Your ability to easily locate the important concepts of a recent lecture will help you move along more rapidly, as you don't have to spend time rereading an entire chapter just to reinforce one point that you may not have completely understood.

This *Guide* is a valuable resource. You've found a wonderful study partner!

Note-Taking Tips

1. It is easier to take notes if you are not hearing the information for the first time. Read the chapter or the material that is about to be discussed before class. This will help you to anticipate what will be said in class and have an idea of what to write down. It will also help to read over your notes from the previous class. This way you can avoid having to spend the first few minutes of class trying to remember where you left off last time.

2. Don't waste your time trying to write down everything that your professor says. Instead, listen closely and write down only the important points. Review these points after class to remind you of related points that were made during the lecture.

3. If the class discussion takes a spontaneous turn, pay attention and participate in the discussion. Only take notes on the conclusions that are relevant to the lecture.

4. Emphasize main points in your notes. You may want to use a highlighter, special notation (asterisks, exclamation points), format (circle, underline), or placement on the page (indented, bulleted). You will find that when you try to recall these points, you will be able to actually picture them on the page.

5. Be sure to copy specific formulas, laws, and theories word-for-word.

6. Hearing something repeated, stressed, or summed up can be a signal that it is an important concept to understand.

7. Organize handouts, study guides, and exams in your notebook along with your lecture notes. It may be helpful to use a three-ring binder, so that you can insert pages wherever you need to.

8. When taking notes, you might find it helpful to leave a wide margin on all four sides of the page. Doing this allows you to note names, dates, definitions, etc. for easy access and studying later. It may also be helpful to make notes of questions you want to ask your professor about or research later, ideas or relationships that you may want to explore more on your own, or concepts that you don't fully understand.

9. It is best to maintain a separate notebook for each class. Labeling and dating your notes can be helpful when you need to look up information from previous lectures.

10. Make your notes legible, and take notes directly in your notebook. Chances are you won't recopy them no matter how noble your intentions. Spend the time you would have spent recopying the notes studying them instead, drawing conclusions and making connections that you didn't have time for in class.

11. Look over your notes after class while the lecture is still fresh in your mind. Fix illegible items and clarify anything you don't understand. Do this again right before the next class.

Notes

Chapter Objectives

- Accurately define the terms *health, community health, population health,* and *public health.*
- Explain the difference between personal and community health activities.
- List and discuss the factors that influence a community's health.

Chapter Objectives

- Briefly relate the history of community/public health, including the recent history of community and public health in the twentieth-century United States.
- Provide a brief overview of the current health status of Americans.
- Describe the status of efforts to improve world health and list some plans for the future.

Chapter Objectives

- Describe the purpose of the *Healthy People 2010* goals and objectives as they apply to the planning process of the health of Americans.
- Briefly describe the impact terrorism has on community/public health.

INTRODUCTION

- Definitions, Concepts, and Principles
- Community Health vs. Personal Health
- Brief History of Community Health
- American Current Health Concerns

DEFINITIONS

- **Health**
  - "A state of complete physical, mental, and social well being and not merely the absence of disease and infirmity" (World Health Organization, 1947)
  - A dynamic state or condition that is multidimensional in nature and results from the adaptation of an individual to his or her environment

Notes

_____

_____

_____

_____

_____

_____

_____

_____

_____

_____

_____

_____

_____

_____

_____

_____

_____

_____

_____

_____

_____

_____

_____

_____

_____

_____

_____

_____

_____

_____

_____

_____

_____

_____

_____

_____

_____

_____

_____

_____

_____

An Introduction to
Community Health Fifth Edition

DEFINITIONS

- **Community**
  - Group of people who have common characteristics
  - Characteristics of communities:
    1. Membership
    2. Common symbol system
    3. Shared values and norms
    4. Mutual influence
    5. Shared needs and commitment
    6. Shared emotional connection

An Introduction to
Community Health Fifth Edition

Definitions

- **Community health**
  - The health status of a defined group of people and the actions and conditions, both private and public (governmental), to promote, protect, and preserve their health

An Introduction to
Community Health Fifth Edition

- **Population health**
  - The health status of people who are not organized and have no identity as a group or locality, and the actions and conditions to promote, protect, and preserve their health
- **Public health**
  - Health status of a defined group of people, and governmental actions and conditions to promote, protect, and preserve the people's health

COMMUNITY HEALTH vs. PERSONAL HEALTH

- PERSONAL

  Individual actions and decision making that affect the health of an individual or his or her immediate family

- COMMUNITY

  Activities aimed at protecting or improving the health of a population or community

FACTORS AFFECTING COMMUNITY HEALTH

PHYSICAL FACTORS

Industrial development

Community size

Environment

Geography

SOCIAL/CULTURAL FACTORS

Beliefs, traditions, and prejudices

Economy, politics, religion

Socioeconomic status

Social norms

HEALTH OF THE COMMUNITY

COMMUNITY ORGANIZATION

Ways in which communities organize their resources

Tax-supported vs. non-tax-supported services

INDIVIDUAL BEHAVIORS

Takes the concerted effort of many—if not most—to make a community voluntary program work

| Prehistory 7000+ B.C. | Hammurabi 1750 B.C. | Greeks 400 B.C. | Middle Ages 410–1500 A.D. |

Egyptians 1500–1050 B.C.   Romans 450 B.C.–410 A.D.

Enlightenment 1700s   20th Century

Renaissance 1500–1700   19th Century   21st Century

An Introduction to
Community Health Fifth Edition

Brief History of Community Health

- EARLIEST CIVILIZATIONS
  - Predate archaeological records
  - Speculate health practices being performed

An Introduction to
Community Health Fifth Edition

Brief History of Community Health

- ANCIENT SOCIETIES (before 500 B.C.)
  - Northern India: Evidence of bathrooms and sewers
  - Middle Kingdom of ancient Egypt: Evidence of water drainage
  - Crete: Evidence of toilets, flushing systems, and sewers
  - Sumarian clay tablet: Evidence of prescription drugs

An Introduction to
Community Health Fifth Edition

Brief History of Community Health

- 1500 B.C. More than 700 drugs were known to the Egyptians.
- Babylon evidence: The Code of Hammurabi contained laws pertaining to physicians and health practices.
- Book of Leviticus provided guidelines for personal cleanliness, sanitation, disinfection of wells, isolation of disease, disposal of refuse, and the hygiene of maternity.

An Introduction to
Community Health Fifth Edition

Brief History of Community Health

- CLASSICAL CULTURES: 500 B.C. to 500 A.D.
  - Greeks: Golden age of Greece; games of strength and skill for men
  - Greeks: Active in community sanitation
  - Greeks: Running water; supplemented local city wells with water supplies from mountains as far as 10 miles away.
  - Romans: Improved on Greek engineering and built aqueducts and sewer systems
  - Romans: Christians built hospitals for the public as charitable organizations

An Introduction to
Community Health Fifth Edition

Brief History of Community Health

- MIDDLE AGES: 500 to 1500 A.D.
  - Growing revulsion of the Roman Empire
  - Spiritual era of public health
  - Great epidemics of plague

An Introduction to
Community Health Fifth Edition

Brief History of Community Health

- RENAISSANCE AND EXPLORATION: 1500 to 1700 A.D.
  - Rebirth of thinking about nature of the world and of humankind
  - Used epidemiology to determine who was getting sick (saints and sinners both)
  - Belief that diseases were caused by environmental, not spiritual, factors
  - Observed the sick, leading to a greater understanding of signs and symptoms of a disease

Notes

_____

_____

_____

_____

_____

_____

_____

_____

_____

_____

_____

_____

_____

_____

_____

_____

_____

_____

_____

_____

_____

_____

_____

_____

_____

_____

_____

_____

_____

_____

_____

_____

_____

_____

_____

_____

_____

_____

An Introduction to
Community Health Fifth Edition

Brief History of Community Health

EIGHTEENTH CENTURY: INDUSTRIAL GROWTH
- Cities overcrowded
  - Water supplies inadequate
  - Streets heaped with trash and garbage
- Occupational health
  - Workplaces unsafe and unhealthy
  - Workforce poor
  - Children forced to work long hours

An Introduction to
Community Health Fifth Edition

Brief History of Community Health

- Medical Advances in the Eighteenth Century
  - 1796: Dr. Edward Jenner developed the small pox vaccination, saving the lives of millions.
  - General George Washington ordered his troops to be vaccinated to ensure their safety.
  - 1798: Marine Hospital Service was formed, leading to the eventual development of the U.S. Public Health Service.

An Introduction to
Community Health Fifth Edition

Brief History of Community Health

NINETEENTH CENTURY
- Early Approach
  - Few advancements in public health
  - Federal government approach "laissez faire"
  - Health quackery thrived
- Epidemics Continued
  - London cholera epidemic struck in 1849
  - Miasmas theory of contagious disease
  - Dr. John Snow and the Broad Street pump

An Introduction to
Community Health Fifth Edition

Brief History of Community Health

- LEMUEL SHATTUCK'S HEALTH REPORT, 1850 (Modern era of public health)
- FIVE PERIODS OF ERA
  - Miasma, 1850 to 1875
  - Bacteriological, 1875 to 1900
  - Health Resources Development, 1900 to 1960
  - Social Engineering, 1960 to 1975
  - Health Promotion, 1975 to present

An Introduction to
Community Health Fifth Edition

HEALTH RESOURCES

- BEGINNING OF TWENTIETH CENTURY
  - Life expectancy less than 50 years
  - Communicable diseases the leading causes of death
  - Children's health concerns

An Introduction to
Community Health Fifth Edition

HEALTH RESOURCES
(1900–1960)

- REFORM PHASE of PUBLIC HEALTH: 1900 to 1920
  - 1900: 38 states had health departments.
  - 1906: Pure Food and Drugs Act (*The Jungle*).
  - 1910: Movement toward healthier conditions in the workplace.
  - Reform movement was broad, involving both social and moral as well as health issues.

Notes

_____
_____
_____
_____
_____
_____
_____
_____
_____
_____
_____
_____
_____
_____
_____
_____
_____
_____
_____
_____
_____
_____
_____
_____
_____
_____
_____
_____
_____
_____
_____
_____
_____
_____
_____
_____
_____
_____
_____
_____
_____
_____
_____

An Introduction to
Community Health Fifth Edition

HEALTH RESOURCES
(1900–1960)

- REFORM PHASE of PUBLIC HEALTH: 1900 to 1920
  - 1917: U.S. ranked 14th of 16 progressive nations in maternal health.
  - 1920: Thomas D. Wood (Father of Health Education) developed the first professional preparation program in health education at Columbia University.

An Introduction to
Community Health Fifth Edition

HEALTH RESOURCES
(1900–1960)

- GREAT DEPRESSION & WORLD WAR II (1929–1935)
  - Social Security Act of 1935.
  - National Institutes of Health established in the 1930s.
  - 1933: Franklin D. Roosevelt created numerous programs for the public works as a part of his New Deal. Much of the money went to health departments.
- THE POSTWAR YEARS (1945–1960)
  - 1946: Communicable Disease Center established.
  - The Hill–Burton Act enhanced the quality of hospitals.
  - 1948: World Health Organization founded.
  - Hospitals were being built .
  - 1950: Vaccine for polio was developed.
  - President Eisenhower's heart attack helped America focus on its number 1 killer.

An Introduction to
Community Health Fifth Edition

HEALTH RESOURCES

- SOCIAL ENGINEERING (1960–1973)
  - 1965: Congress passed Medicare and Medicaid bills.
  - 1970: OSHA Act signed.
- HEALTH PROMOTION PERIOD (1975–1990)
  - Healthy People
  - Lifestyle-related diseases
  - High medical care costs

Notes

_____

Community Health
in the Early 2000s

- Health Problems
  - Health care costs
  - Environmental concerns
  - Lifestyle diseases
  - Emerging and re-emerging communicable diseases
  - Substance abuse problems
  - Terrorism

Health Care Delivery

- Rising health care costs
- Insured versus the uninsured
- Access issues

Environmental Problems

- Air
- Water
- Damaged natural resources
- Must improve our conservation of resources
- Overpopulation

Notes

_____

_____

_____

_____

_____

_____

_____

_____

_____

_____

_____

_____

_____

_____

_____

_____

_____

_____

_____

_____

_____

_____

_____

_____

_____

_____

_____

_____

_____

_____

_____

_____

_____

_____

_____

_____

_____

_____

_____

_____

_____

An Introduction to
Community Health Fifth Edition

Lifestyle Diseases

- Obesity: Type II diabetes
- Heart disease
- Cancer
- Stroke
- Chronic lower respiratory disease
- Need better control of behavioral lifestyle, such as exercise, diet, and use of tobacco, alcohol, or other drugs

An Introduction to
Community Health Fifth Edition

Communicable Diseases

- Infectious types of disease
- Drug-resistant forms
- New diseases such as severe acute respiratory syndrome (SARS)
- Bioterrorism

An Introduction to
Community Health Fifth Edition

Terrorism

- Possible agents
  - Chemical
  - Nuclear
  - Biological

An Introduction to
Community Health Fifth Edition

Community Health in the 21st Century

- World Planning
  - Reduce the burden of excess mortality and morbidity
  - Counter potential threats to individual health
  - Develop effective health systems
  - Expand the knowledge base

An Introduction to
Community Health Fifth Edition

HEALTH PROMOTION

- LIFESTYLE CHANGES
  - 1977: World Health Organization's "Health for All"
  - 1979: Promoting Health/Preventing Disease: Objectives for the Nation
    - 226 objectives based on preventive services, health protection, and health promotion
  - Healthy People 2000
    - More than 300 objectives
  - Healthy People 2010

Chapter 2: Organizations That Help Shape Community Health

Notes

_____

_____

_____

_____

_____

_____

_____

_____

_____

_____

_____

_____

_____

_____

_____

_____

_____

_____

_____

_____

_____

_____

_____

_____

_____

_____

_____

_____

_____

_____

_____

_____

_____

_____

_____

_____

_____

_____

Chapter Objectives

- Explain the need for organizing to improve community health.
- Explain what a governmental health organization is and give examples.
- Explain the role the World Health Organization (WHO) plays in community health.

Chapter Objectives

- Briefly describe the structure and function of the United States Department of Health and Human Services (HHS).
- State the three core functions of public health.
- List the 10 essential public health services.
- Explain the relationship between a state and local health department.

Notes

_____

_____

_____

_____

_____

_____

_____

_____

_____

_____

_____

_____

_____

_____

_____

_____

_____

_____

_____

_____

_____

_____

_____

_____

_____

_____

_____

_____

_____

_____

_____

_____

_____

_____

_____

_____

_____

_____

_____

_____

_____

An Introduction to
Community Health Fifth Edition

Chapter Objectives

- Explain what is meant by the term _coordinated school health program_.
- Define the term _quasi-governmental_ and explain why some health organizations are classified under this term.

An Introduction to
Community Health Fifth Edition

Chapter Objectives

- List four primary activities of most voluntary health organizations.
- Identify major professional health organizations and foundations that support community health efforts.
- Explain how philanthropic foundations contribute to community health.

An Introduction to
Community Health Fifth Edition

Chapter Objectives

- Discuss the role that service, social, and religious organizations play in community health.
- Identify the major reason why corporations are involved in community health and describe some corporate activities that contribute to community health.

Notes

_____

_____

_____

_____

_____

_____

_____

_____

_____

_____

_____

_____

_____

_____

_____

_____

_____

_____

_____

_____

_____

_____

_____

_____

_____

_____

_____

_____

_____

_____

_____

_____

_____

Introduction

- Today's Communities
  - More educated, mobile, and more independent than past communities
  - In need of better long-term planning and community organizing due to the large size of today's communities
  - Highly developed and centralized resources in our national institutions and organizations
  - Continued concentration of wealth and population in the largest metropolitan areas
  - Rapid movement of information, resources, and people
  - Limited horizontal relationships among organizations
  - Top-down funding for many community programs

Communities' Ability to Respond to a Health Crisis

- Communities' ability to respond to a health crisis is hindered by the following characteristics:
  - Highly developed and centralized resources in our national institutions and organizations
  - Continued concentration of wealth and population in the largest metropolitan areas
  - Rapid movement of information, resources, and people
  - Limited horizontal relationships among organizations
  - Top-down funding for many community programs

Governmental Health Agencies

- Funded primarily by tax dollars
- Managed by governmental officials
- Authority for some area of health
- Levels
  - International
  - National
  - State
  - Local

World Health Organization

- HISTORY
  - United Nations charter in 1945 established the need
  - Officially began April 7, 1948—World Health Day
  - Guided by the United Nations Millennium Declaration in 2000
- ORGANIZATION
  - Open membership
  - Headquarters located in Geneva, Switzerland
  - World Health Assembly
  - Administered by director-general and 5 assistant directors-general
- PURPOSE
  - Attainment by all peoples of the best possible level of health

World Health Organization

- Six Core Functions
  - Articulating consistent, ethical, and evidence-based policy and advocacy positions
  - Assessing trends and comparing performance; setting agenda for and stimulating new research
  - Catalyzing change through technical and policy support
  - Negotiating and sustaining global partnerships
  - Setting, validating, monitoring, and pursuing the proper implementation of norms and standards
  - Development and testing of new technologies, tools, guidelines for disease control, risk reduction, health care management, and service delivery

National Health Agencies

- Department of Health and Human Services
  - Principal agency for protecting the health of all Americans and providing essential human services
  - Other agencies also contribute to our Nation's health
    - Women, Infants, and Children (WIC) program
    - Occupational Safety and Health Administration (OSHA)
    - Environmental Protection Agency (EPA)
- Organizational Structure
  - 12 operating divisions

Notes

_____

_____

_____

_____

_____

_____

_____

_____

_____

_____

_____

_____

_____

_____

_____

_____

_____

_____

_____

_____

_____

_____

_____

_____

_____

_____

_____

_____

_____

_____

_____

_____

_____

_____

_____

_____

_____

An Introduction to
Community Health Fifth Edition

Organizational Chart

Secretary

Deputy Secretary

Director, Intergovernmental Affairs, & Secretary's Regional Representatives

Chief of Staff

Executive Secretary

An Introduction to
Community Health Fifth Edition

Administration for Children and Families (ACF)

- **Responsible for providing direction and leadership for all federal programs for needy children and families (administers Head Start program).**

An Introduction to
Community Health Fifth Edition

Administration on Aging (AoA)

- **Supports a nationwide aging network, providing services to the elderly, especially to enable them to remain independent. Supports services and provides leadership on aging issues.**

An Introduction to
Community Health Fifth Edition

Centers for Medicare and Medicaid (CMS)

- **Administers the Medicare and Medicaid Programs, which provide health care coverage to about 75 million Americans.**

An Introduction to
Community Health Fifth Edition

Healthcare Research and Quality (AHRQ)

- **The lead agency charged with supporting research designed to improve the quality of health care, reduce its costs, improve patient safety, decrease medical errors, and broaden access.**

An Introduction to
Community Health Fifth Edition

Centers for Disease Control and Prevention (CDC)

- **Serves as the national focus for developing and applying disease prevention and control, environmental health, and health promotion and health education activities designed to improve the health of the people of the United States.**

Notes

Agency for Toxic Substances and Disease Registry (ATSDR)

- **Working with states and other federal agencies, ATSDR deals with the cleanup of hazardous substances in the environment.**

Food and Drug Administration (FDA)

- **Mission is to promote and protect public health by helping safe and effective products reach the market in a timely way and by monitoring products for continued safety after they are in use.**

Health Resources and Services Administration (HRSA)

- **Helps provide health resources for medically underserved populations. Works to build the health care workforce.**

Indian Health Service (IHS)

- **Provides comprehensive health service delivery system to American Indians and Alaska Natives.**

National Institutes of Health (NIH)

- **The world's premier medical research organization, supporting research projects nationwide.**

Substance Abuse and Mental Health Services Administration (SAMHSA)

- **Ensures up-to-date information and state-of-the-art practice is effectively used for the prevention and treatment of addictive and mental disorders.**

An Introduction to
Community Health Fifth Edition

Program Support Center (PSC)

- **Provides qualitative and responsive administrative support services on a cost-effective, competitive, fee-for-service basis to HHS components and other federal agencies.**

An Introduction to
Community Health Fifth Edition

State Health Agencies

- **PURPOSE: To promote, protect, and maintain the health and welfare of their citizens**
- **CORE FUNCTIONS**
  - **Assessment**
  - **Policy development**
  - **Assurance**

An Introduction to
Community Health Fifth Edition

State Health Agencies

■ Assurance

Monitor Health

■ Assessment

Evaluate

Assure Competent Workforce

Diagnose & Investigate

System Research Management

Inform, Educate, Empower

Link to/ Provide Care

Policy Development

Enforce Laws

Mobilize Community Partnerships

Develop Policies

Notes

An Introduction to
Community Health Fifth Edition

State Health Agencies

- DIVISIONS OR BUREAUS
  - Administration
  - Communicable and chronic disease prevention and control
  - Vital and health statistics
  - Public health nursing
  - Environmental health

An Introduction to
Community Health Fifth Edition

State Health Agencies

- DIVISIONS OR BUREAUS (Continued)
  - Health education or promotion
  - Maternal and child health
  - Mental health
  - Occupational and industrial health
  - Laboratory services
  - Health services
  - Veterinary public health

An Introduction to
Community Health Fifth Edition

Organization of Local Health Departments

Board

Health Commissoner | Health Officer (Physician)

Environmental Health | Health Education | Nursing | Vital Statistics | Chronic Disease | Communicable Disease

Notes

_____

_____

_____

_____

_____

_____

_____

_____

_____

_____

_____

_____

_____

_____

_____

_____

_____

_____

_____

_____

_____

_____

_____

_____

_____

_____

_____

_____

_____

_____

_____

_____

_____

_____

_____

Local Health Agencies

FUNDING
  Major portion comes from local property taxes
  Some state and federal dollars
  Some programs on fee-for-service basis
  Sliding scales determine the fee for service

COORDINATED SCHOOL HEALTH PROGRAM
  Health education
  Healthful school environment
  Health services

Coordinated School Health Program

- An organized set of policies, procedures, and activities designed to protect, promote, and improve the health and well-being of students and staff, thus improving the student's ability to learn.
- Components
  - School health education
  - Health services
  - School environment
  - Counseling
  - Psychological and social services
  - Physical education
  - School nutrition
  - Family and community
  - Health promotion

Barriers to Coordinated School Health Programs

1. Insufficient local administrative support
2. Inadequately prepared teachers
3. Too few school days to teach in the school year
4. Inadequate funding
5. The lack of credibility of health education as an academic subject
6. Insufficient community/parental support
7. Concern for the teaching of controversial topics such as sex education

_____

_____

_____

_____

_____

_____

_____

_____

_____

_____

_____

_____

_____

_____

_____

_____

_____

_____

_____

_____

_____

_____

_____

_____

_____

_____

_____

_____

_____

_____

_____

_____

_____

_____

An Introduction to
Community Health Fifth Edition

Quasi-governmental Organizations

- QUASI-GOVERNMENTAL HEALTH AGENCIES
  - Some responsibilities assigned by government but operate more like voluntary agencies
  - Funded by tax dollars and private sources
  - Operate independently of government supervision
- AMERICAN RED CROSS
- NATIONAL SCIENCE FOUNDATION
- NATIONAL ACADEMY OF SCIENCES

An Introduction to
Community Health Fifth Edition

American Red Cross

- Founded in 1881 by Clara Barton
- Official Duties
  - Provide relief to victims of natural disasters
  - Serve as a liaison between member of the active military and their families during emergencies
- Additional Duties
  - Blood drives, safety services, nursing and health services, youth services, community volunteer services, and international services

An Introduction to
Community Health Fifth Edition

National Science Foundation

- Purpose
  - Funding and promotion of scientific research and development of individual scientists

Notes

_____

_____

_____

_____

_____

_____

_____

_____

_____

_____

_____

_____

_____

_____

_____

_____

_____

_____

_____

_____

_____

_____

_____

_____

_____

_____

_____

_____

_____

_____

_____

_____

An Introduction to
Community Health Fifth Edition

National Academy of Sciences

- Purpose
  - Acts as an advisor to the government on questions dealing with science and technology

An Introduction to
Community Health Fifth Edition

Nongovernmental Health Agencies

- NONGOVERNMENTAL HEALTH AGENCIES
  - Funded by private donations
- VOLUNTARY HEALTH AGENCIES
  - Created by concerned citizens to deal with a health need not met by governmental health agencies
- ORGANIZATION
  - National
  - State
  - Local

An Introduction to
Community Health Fifth Edition

Voluntary Health Agencies

- PURPOSE
  - Raise money to fund programs
  - Provide education both to professionals and to the public
  - Provide services to those individuals and families that are afflicted with the health problem
- LARGEST VOLUNTARY HEALTH AGENCIES
  - American Cancer Society
  - American Heart Association
  - American Lung Association

Nongovernmental Health Agencies

- PROFESSIONAL HEALTH ORGANIZATIONS/ASSOCIATIONS
  - Mission: Promote high standards of professional practice for their specific profession
    - American Public Health Association
    - American Medical Association
    - American Nursing Association
    - American Dental Association
    - Society for Public Health Education, Inc.

Nongovernmental Health Agencies

- PHILANTHROPIC FOUNDATIONS
  - Provide funding for research and programming
    - Rockefeller Foundation
    - Robert Wood Johnson Foundation
    - Henry J. Kaiser Family Foundation
    - W. K. Kellogg Foundation

Nongovernmental Health Agencies

- SERVICE, SOCIAL, AND RELIGIOUS ORGANIZATIONS
  - Jaycees
  - Kiwanis Club
  - Rotary Club
  - Shriners
  - American Legion
- CORPORATE INVOLVEMENT
  - Worksite programs
  - Sponsorship of health-enhancing activities in the community

Chapter 3: Epidemiology: The Study of Disease, Injury, and Death in the Community

Notes

_____

_____

_____

_____

_____

_____

_____

_____

_____

_____

_____

_____

_____

_____

_____

_____

_____

_____

_____

_____

_____

_____

_____

_____

_____

_____

_____

_____

_____

_____

_____

_____

_____

_____

_____

_____

_____

_____

An Introduction to **Community Health** Fifth Edition

James F. McKenzie · Robert R. Pinger · Jerome E. Kotecki

An Introduction to **Community Health** Fifth Edition

Chapter Objectives

- Define the terms *epidemic, epidemiology,* and *epidemiologist,* and explain their importance in community health.
- List some diseases that caused epidemics in the past and some that are causing epidemics today.
- Discuss how the practice of epidemiology has changed since the days of Benjamin Rush and John Snow.

An Introduction to **Community Health** Fifth Edition

Chapter Objectives

- Explain why rates are important in epidemiology and list some of the commonly used rates.
- Define incidence and prevalence rates and provide an example of each
- Calculate a variety of rates from the appropriate data.
- Discuss the importance of disease reporting to a community's health and describe the reporting process.

Chapter Objectives

- Identify sources of standardized data used by epidemiologists, community health workers, and health officials and list the types of data available from each source.
- Define the following standardized measurements of health status: life expectancy, years of potential life lost (YPLL), and disability-adjusted life expectancy (DALEs).

Chapter Objectives

- List and describe the three types of epidemiological studies and explain the purpose of each

Epidemiologists

- Primary concern is the course of disease in a population
- Study outbreaks of disease, injury, and death in the human population
- Questions asked by epidemiologists:
  - How many people are sick?
  - Who is sick?
  - When did people get sick?
  - Where did people get sick?
  - What do the sick people have in common?
- Nickname for the profession is "population medicine"

Notes

Definitions

Epidemiology
- "The study of the distribution and determinants of diseases and injuries in human populations." Mausner & Kramer, 1985

Endemic Disease
- A disease that occurs regularly in a population

Epidemic
- An unexpectedly large number of cases of disease in a particular population

Recent Epidemics in the United States

Disease	Cases/Prev. yrs	Period	# of Cases
St. Louis encephalitis	5/72	1975	1,815
Legionnaires'	Unknown	1976	235
AIDS	Unknown	1981-1999	733,374
Lyme disease	Unknown	1990-1999	121,000

Definitions

Epidemiologist
- One who practices epidemiology

Epizootiologist
- One who studies disease outbreaks in animals

Pandemic
- An outbreak of disease over a wide geographical area such as a continent (the influenza pandemic of 1918–1919 killed 25 million people worldwide)

Notes

History of Epidemiology

- 300 B.C.: Hippocrates, "Father of Medicine," suggested a relationship between the occurrence of disease and the physical environment.
- With the fall of Greece and Rome, there were few advancements in health and medicine, and diseases became linked to the spiritual world.
- 1793: Yellow fever in Philadelphia
  - Killed 4,044 people
  - Cause (mosquito) discovered in 1901 by Major Walter Reed
- 1849: Cholera in London
  - Dr. John Snow investigated
  - Broad street pump
  - 30 years before Louis Pasteur's "germ theory of disease"

Numbers and Rates

- Case Definition or "What"
  - A set of criteria for deciding whether a person has a particular disease or other health-related condition
- Rates
  - The number of events that occur in a given population in a given period of time
- Importance of Rates
  - Allow for a comparison of outbreaks that occur at different times or in different places

Definitions

- Acute: Diseases whose peak severity of symptoms occurs and subsides within days or weeks
- Chronic: Diseases that usually last three months or longer
- Notifiable diseases: Infectious diseases that can become epidemic
  - National Electronic Telecommunication System (NETS): Tracks notifiable diseases
  - CDC, *Morbidity and Mortality Weekly Report* (MMWR)

Notes

An Introduction to
Community Health Fifth Edition

3 Important Kinds of Rates

Natality (birth) rate = $\dfrac{\text{No. of live births to residents in an area in a calendar year}}{\text{Population in the area in the same year}}$

Morbidity (disease) rate = $\dfrac{\text{No. of cases of residents with illness in an area in a calendar year}}{\text{Population in the area in the same year}}$

Mortality (fatality) rate = $\dfrac{\text{No. of deaths to residents in an area in a calendar year}}{\text{Population in the area in the same year}}$

An Introduction to
Community Health Fifth Edition

3 Important Morbidity Rates

Incidence rate = $\dfrac{\text{No. of new cases of a disease in a certain time period}}{\text{Population at risk in same time period}}$

Prevalence rate = $\dfrac{\text{No. of new and old cases of a disease in a certain time period}}{\text{Population at risk in same time period}}$

Attack rate = $\dfrac{\text{No. of new cases in a narrowly defined population during a specific time period}}{\text{Population at risk in same time period}}$

An Introduction to
Community Health Fifth Edition

3 Important Mortality Rates

Crude death rate = $\dfrac{\text{Number of deaths (all causes)}}{\text{Estimated midyear population}}$

Age-specific death rate = $\dfrac{\text{Number of deaths (35–44)}}{\text{Estimated midyear population (35–44)}}$

Cause-specific death rate = $\dfrac{\text{Number of deaths (specific cause)}}{\text{Estimated midyear population}}$

Additional Rates

- Case fatality rate
  - The percentage of cases that resulted in death
- Proportionate mortality rate
  - Describes the relationship between the number of deaths from a specific cause and the total number of deaths attributed to all causes

An Introduction to
Community Health Fifth Edition

Reporting Births, Deaths, & Diseases

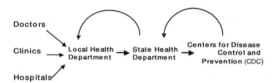

An Introduction to
Community Health Fifth Edition

Sources of Standardized Data

- U.S. Census
  - Conducted every 10 years; enumeration of population
- Statistical Abstract of the United States
  - Statistics on social, political, and economic organization
- Vital Statistics
  - Statistical summaries of records of major life events

Notes

Sources of Standardized Data

- Morbidity & Mortality Weekly Reports (MMWR)
  - Lists cases of notifiable diseases in the United States
- National Health Surveys
  - Health interviews of people
  - Clinical tests, measurement, and physical examinations
  - Survey of places where people receive medical care
  - Other types of health surveys:
    - NHIS   NHANES   BRFSS   YBRS   NHCS

Standardized Measurements of Health Status

- Mortality statistics
- Life expectancy
- Years of potential life lost (YPLL)
- Disability-adjusted life years (DALY)
- Disability-adjusted life expectancy (DALE)

Epidemiological Study Measures

- Probability statements or testing the differences in groups
- Cohort study
  - Relative risk: Measure of association between incidence of disease in unexposed group & exposed group
- Case control study
  - Odds ratio: Estimates "relative risk" because incidence measures cannot be obtained from two groups
- Experimental
  - Use statistical t-test, or F-test to test probability of differences between groups

An Introduction to
Community Health Fifth Edition

Epidemiological Studies

- Descriptive Studies
  - "Who," or person
    - Age, sex, ethnic, race, socioeconomic status
  - "When," or time
    - Time of day, week, month, season, year, decades
    - Incubation period
  - "Where," or place
    - Country, state, county, street, urban or rural, domestic or foreign, institutional or noninstitutional

An Introduction to
Community Health Fifth Edition

Epidemiological Studies

- Descriptive Studies
  - Epidemic curve: Graphic display of the cases of disease by the time or date of the onset of the symptoms
    - Two classical types
      - Point source epidemic curve: Each case can be traced to an exposure to the same source. Includes the incubation period, which is the period of time between exposure to an infectious agent and the onset of symptoms.
      - Propagated epidemic curve: Cases appear first at the end of the incubation period following exposure to an infected source.

An Introduction to
Community Health Fifth Edition

Epidemiological Studies

- Analytical Studies: Testing of hypotheses about relationships between health problems and possible risk factors
  - Two basic types
    - Case control study (retrospective)
      - Identify familial, environmental, or behavioral factors that are common in a case group but not in the controlled group
    - Cohort study (prospective study)
      - Large number of subjects sharing similar experiences. The subjects are classified on the basis of their exposure to one or more causative factors of a illness or disease. The subjects are observed for a number of years to examine rates of disease associated with a causative factor.

Notes

Epidemiological Studies

- Experimental
  - A study carried out under controlled conditions
  - Control group
  - Treatment group
  - Placebo

Chapter 4: Epidemiology: Prevention and Control of Diseases and Health Conditions

Notes

Chapter Objectives

- **Explain the difference between communicable and noncommunicable diseases and between acute and chronic diseases.**
- **Describe and explain communicable and multicausation disease models.**
- **Explain why noncommunicable diseases are a community health concern and provide some examples of communicable and some examples of important noncommunicable diseases.**

Chapter Objectives

- **Explain how communicable diseases are transmitted in a community using the "chain of infection" model and use a specific communicable disease to illustrate your explanation.**
- **Explain the difference between primary, secondary, and tertiary prevention of disease.**

An Introduction to
Community Health Fifth Edition

Chapter Objectives

- List and explain the various criteria that communities might use in order to prioritize their health problems in preparation for the allocation of prevention and control resources
- List and discuss the measures for preventing and controlling the spread of communicable diseases in a community.

An Introduction to
Community Health Fifth Edition

Chapter Objectives

- List and discuss approaches to non-communicable disease control in a community.
- Define and explain the purpose and importance of health screenings.
- Outline a chronic, noncommunicable disease control program that includes primary, secondary, and tertiary disease prevention components.

An Introduction to
Community Health Fifth Edition

Classification of Diseases and Health Problems

Four Classification Schemes

1. Organ or organ system
   - For example, heart disease, kidney disease, respiratory infection
2. Causative agent
   - Biological agents
   - Chemical agents
   - Physical agents

Notes

_____
_____
_____
_____
_____
_____
_____
_____
_____
_____
_____
_____
_____
_____
_____
_____
_____
_____
_____
_____
_____
_____
_____
_____
_____
_____
_____
_____
_____
_____
_____
_____
_____
_____
_____
_____
_____
_____

Causative Agents for Diseases and Injuries

Biological Agents	Chemical Agents	Physical Agents
Viruses	Pesticides	Heat
Rickettsiae	Food additives	Light
Bacteria	Pharmacologics	Radiation
Fungi	Industrial chemicals	Noise
Protozoa	Air pollutants	Vibration
Metazoa	Cigarette smoke	Speeding object

Classification of Diseases and Health Problems

3. Communicable vs. noncommunicable
4. Acute vs. chronic
   - Peak symptoms within 3 months (acute) or longer than 3 months (chronic)

Types of Diseases	Examples
Acute Diseases	
Communicable	Common cold, pneumonia, mumps, measles, pertussis, typhoid fever, cholera
Noncommunicable	Appendicitis, poisoning, trauma
Chronic Diseases	
Communicable	Tuberculosis, AIDS, Lyme disease, syphilis, rheumatic fever
Noncommunicable	Diabetes, coronary heart disease, osteoarthritis, cirrhosis of the liver

Notes

An Introduction to
Community Health Fifth Edition

Communicable Disease Model

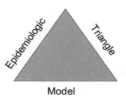

An Introduction to
Community Health Fifth Edition

Communicable Disease Model

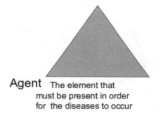

Agent   The element that
must be present in order
for the diseases to occur

An Introduction to
Community Health Fifth Edition

Communicable Disease Model

Host   Any susceptible
organism invaded
by an infectious agent

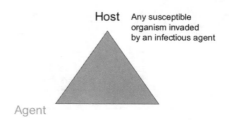

Agent

Notes

Communicable Disease Model

Host

Agent   Environment
All other factors that inhibit
or promote disease
transmission

Chain of Infection

A model to conceptualize the transmission of a
communicable disease from its source to a susceptible host

Chain of Infection

Pathogen

- The disease-causing agent

Notes

Chain of Infection

Pathogen Reservoir

- **The habitat in which an infectious agent normally lives and grows**
  - **Human: Anthroponoses, symptomatic or asymptomatic**
  - **Animal: Zoonoses**
  - **Environmental: Plants, soil, and water**

Chain of Infection

Pathogen Reservoir Portal of exit

- **The path by which an agent leaves the source host**

Chain of Infection

Pathogen Reservoir Portal of exit Trans-mission How pathogens are passed

Modes of Transmission
Direct: Immediate transfer
- **Direct contact**
- **Droplet spread**

Indirect
- **Airborne**
- **Vehicleborne**
- **Vectorborne**

Chain of Infection

Pathogen · Reservoir · Portal of exit · Trans-mission · **Portal of entry**

- Agent enters
susceptible host

Respiratory
Oral
Skin
Intravenous
Gastrointestinal

Chain of Infection

Pathogen · Reservoir · Portal of exit · Trans-mission · Portal of entry · **New host**

- Final link is
a susceptible host

Noncommunicable Disease Model

Your genetic
endowment

_____

_____

_____

_____

_____

_____

_____

_____

_____

_____

_____

_____

_____

_____

_____

_____

_____

_____

_____

_____

_____

_____

_____

_____

_____

_____

_____

_____

_____

_____

_____

_____

_____

_____

_____

_____

_____

An Introduction to
Community Health Fifth Edition

Noncommunicable Disease Model

Personality
Beliefs
Your genetic endowment
Behavioral choices

An Introduction to
Community Health Fifth Edition

Noncommunicable Disease Model

Environment
Health Care System
Economics
Personality
Beliefs
Your genetic endowment
Water Quality
Behavioral choices
Air Pollution

An Introduction to
Community Health Fifth Edition

Diseases of the Heart and Blood

- Coronary heart disease (CHD): Characterized by damage to the coronary arteries.
- Atherosclerosis: Narrowing of the blood vessels resulting from the build-up of fatty deposits on the walls of the blood vessel.
- Cerebrovascular disease (stroke): Blood supply to the brain is disrupted.

Notes

_____

An Introduction to
Community Health Fifth Edition

Cancer

- Malignant neoplasm: Occurs when cells lose control over their growth and division. As these cells continue to grow they eventually develop a "new growth"—a tumor
- Metastasis: Parts of the tumor break off and travel to the rest of the body's organs and continue their growth.

An Introduction to
Community Health Fifth Edition

Other Top Noncommunicable Diseases

1. Chronic obstructive pulmonary disease
2. Diabetes mellitus
3. Chronic liver disease and cirrhosis

An Introduction to
Community Health Fifth Edition

Prioritizing Prevention and Control Efforts

- Leading causes of death
- Years of potential life lost
- Economic cost to society

Notes

_____
_____
_____
_____
_____
_____
_____
_____
_____
_____
_____
_____
_____
_____
_____
_____
_____
_____
_____
_____
_____
_____
_____
_____
_____
_____
_____
_____
_____
_____
_____
_____
_____
_____
_____
_____
_____
_____

An Introduction to
Community Health Fifth Edition

Prevention, Intervention, Control, and Eradication of Diseases

- Prevention
  - Primary
  - Secondary
  - Tertiary
- Intervention
  - Defined as taking action during an event
- Control
  - General term used in the containment of disease
- Eradication
  - Total elimination of the disease

An Introduction to
Community Health Fifth Edition

Levels of Prevention

- Primary Prevention
  - The forestalling of the onset of illness or injury during the pre-pathogenesis period (before the disease process begins)
- Secondary Prevention
  - The early diagnosis and prompt treatment of diseases before the disease becomes advanced and disability becomes severe
- Tertiary Prevention
  - The retraining, reeducation, and rehabilitation of the patient who has already incurred disability

An Introduction to
Community Health Fifth Edition

Prevention of Communicable Diseases

- Pathogen
  - Pasteurization
  - Chlorination
  - Antibiotics
  - Antivirals
  - Disinfectants

Notes

_____
_____
_____
_____
_____
_____
_____
_____
_____
_____
_____
_____
_____
_____
_____
_____
_____
_____
_____
_____
_____
_____
_____
_____
_____
_____
_____
_____
_____
_____
_____
_____
_____
_____

An Introduction to
Community Health Fifth Edition

Prevention of Communicable Diseases

- Human Reservoir
  - Isolation
  - Surveillance
  - Quarantine
  - Drug treatment

An Introduction to
Community Health Fifth Edition

Prevention of Communicable Diseases

- Portal of Exit
  - Gowns
  - Masks
  - Condoms
  - Hair nets
  - Insect repellents

An Introduction to
Community Health Fifth Edition

Prevention of Communicable Diseases

- Transmission
  - Isolation
  - Hand washing
  - Vector control
  - Sanitary engineering
  - Sneeze glass
  - Sexual abstinence
  - Safer sex

Notes

Prevention of Communicable Diseases

- Portal of Entry
  - Masks
  - Condoms
  - Safety glasses
  - Insect repellents

Prevention of Communicable Diseases

- Establishment of Disease in New Host
  - Immunizations
  - Health education
  - Nutrition promotion
  - Sexual abstinence

Prevention of Noncommunicable Diseases

- Primary Prevention
  - Adequate food intake
  - Good opportunities for education, employment, and housing
  - Efficient community services
  - Health promotion
  - Access to medical services
  - Protection from the environment
  - Protection from occupational hazards
  - Empowerment for one's own health

Notes

_____

_____

_____

_____

_____

_____

_____

_____

_____

_____

_____

_____

_____

_____

_____

_____

_____

_____

_____

_____

_____

_____

_____

Prevention of Noncommunicable Diseases

- Secondary Prevention
  - Mass screenings
  - Case-finding measures
  - Adequate health personnel, equipment, and facilities
  - Personal screening (self breast or testes exams)
  - Hemoccult tests
  - Pap tests

Prevention of Noncommunicable Diseases

- Tertiary Prevention
  - Adequate emergency medical personnel, services, and facilities
  - Understand unmodifiable risk factors
  - Significant behavioral or lifestyle changes (Modifiable risk factors)
  - Support groups
  - Counseling

Chapter 5: Community Organizing/Building and Health Promotion Programming

Notes

Chapter Objectives

- Define community organizing, community capacity, community participation, and empowerment of the community.
- Identify the assumptions that underlie the process of community organization.
- Briefly explain the difference between locality development, social planning, and social action approaches to community organization.
- Explain the difference between needs-based community organizing models.

Chapter Objectives

- List the steps for a generalized model for community organizing/building.
- Explain what is meant by community building.
- Explain the difference between health education and health promotion.
- State and summarize the steps involved in creating a health promotion program.
- Define the term *needs assessment*.

Notes

_____
_____
_____
_____
_____
_____
_____
_____
_____
_____
_____
_____
_____
_____
_____
_____
_____
_____
_____
_____
_____
_____
_____
_____
_____
_____
_____
_____
_____
_____
_____
_____
_____
_____
_____
_____

Chapter Objectives

- Briefly explain the six steps used in assessing needs.
- Explain the difference between goals and objectives.
- List the different type of intervention strategies.
- Explain the purposes of pilot testing in program development.
- State the difference between formative and summative evaluation.

Community Organizing

- Community health problems can be small, only involving a few people, or can be very large, encompassing everyone in the community.
- *Community organizing* was a term coined by American social workers in the 1880s to describe their coordination efforts for newly arrived immigrants and the poor.

Definition

- Community organizing
  - "A process through which communities are helped to identify common problems or goals, mobilize resources, and in other ways develop and implement strategies for reaching their goals they have collectively set."

Notes

_____

_____

_____

_____

_____

_____

_____

_____

_____

_____

_____

_____

_____

_____

_____

_____

_____

_____

_____

_____

_____

_____

_____

_____

_____

_____

_____

_____

_____

_____

_____

_____

_____

_____

Definitions (continued)

- Community capacity: "Community characteristics affecting its ability to identify, mobilize, and address problems.
- Community participation: "A process of involving people in the institutions or decisions that affect their lives."
- Empowered community: "One in which individuals and organizations apply their skills and resources in collective efforts to meet their respective needs."

Assumptions of Community Organization

1. Communities of people can develop the capacity to deal with their own problems.
2. People want to change and can change.
3. People should participate in making, adjusting, or controlling the major changes taking place in their communities.
4. Changes in community living that are self-imposed or self-developed have a meaning and permanence that imposed changes do not have.

Assumptions of Community Organization

5. A "holistic approach" can deal successfully with problems with which a "fragmented approach" cannot cope.
6. Democracy requires cooperative participation and action in the affairs of the community, and people must learn the skills that make this possible.
7. Frequently, communities of people need help in organizing to deal with their needs, just as many individuals require help with individual problems.

Notes

An Introduction to
Community Health Fifth Edition

Community Organizing Methods

- Locality development
  - A broad self-help method in which local citizens develop new skills and become more self-sufficient
- Social planning
  - Utilizes skilled volunteers in the community in a technical process of problem solving
- Social action
  - A technique that involves the redistribution of power and resources to disadvantaged segments of the population

An Introduction to
Community Health Fifth Edition

Steps in Community Organizing

- Recognizing the issue
- Gaining entry into the community
- Organizing the people
- Assessing the community
- Determining the priorities and setting goals
- Arriving at a solution and selecting intervention strategies
- Implementing the plan
- Evaluating the outcomes of the plan of action
- Maintaining the outcomes in the community
- Looping back

An Introduction to
Community Health Fifth Edition

The Final Four Steps

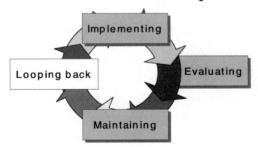

Notes

_____

Creating a Health Promotion Program

Assessing needs	Identifying the problem	Setting goals & objectives	Developing an intervention	Implementing the intervention	Evaluating the results

A Generalized Model for Program Planning

Creating a Health Promotion/ Disease Prevention Program: Overview

- Assessing the needs
- Identifying the problem(s)
- Setting goals and objectives
- Developing an intervention
- Implementing the intervention
- Evaluating the results

Assessing the Needs

Determining the purpose & scope

Gathering data

Analyzing the data

Identifying factors linked to the health problem

Identifying the program focus

Validating the prioritized need

Notes

_____

_____

_____

_____

_____

_____

_____

_____

_____

_____

_____

_____

_____

_____

_____

_____

_____

_____

_____

_____

_____

_____

_____

_____

_____

_____

_____

_____

_____

_____

_____

_____

_____

_____

_____

_____

_____

_____

_____

_____

Questions to Be Asked After the Needs Assessment

- Who is the priority population?
- What are the needs of the priority population?
- Which subgroups within the priority population have the greatest need?
- Where are the subgroups located geographically?
- What is currently being done to resolve identified needs?
- How well have the identified needs been addressed in the past?

Creating a Health Promotion/ Disease Prevention Program: Overview

- Assessing the needs
- Setting goals and objectives
  - A goal is a future event toward which an endeavor is directed.
  - Objectives are steps taken in pursuit of a goal.
- Developing an intervention
  - Designing activities that meet your objectives
- Implementing the intervention
  - Putting into practice
- Evaluating the results
  - Formative evaluation
  - Summative evaluation

Hierarchy of Program Objectives

1. Process/administration objectives
2. Learning objectives
3. Action/behavioral objectives
4. Environmental objectives
5. Program objectives

Notes

_____
_____
_____
_____
_____
_____
_____
_____
_____
_____
_____
_____
_____
_____
_____
_____
_____
_____
_____
_____
_____
_____
_____
_____
_____
_____
_____
_____
_____
_____
_____
_____
_____
_____
_____
_____

An Introduction to
Community Health Fifth Edition

Evaluating the results

Planning the evaluation

An Introduction to
Community Health Fifth Edition

Evaluating the results

Planning the evaluation

Collecting the data

An Introduction to
Community Health Fifth Edition

Evaluating the results

Planning the evaluation

Collecting the data

Analyzing the data

Notes

_____

_____

_____

_____

_____

_____

_____

_____

_____

_____

_____

_____

_____

_____

_____

_____

_____

_____

_____

_____

_____

_____

_____

_____

_____

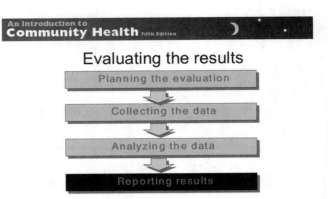

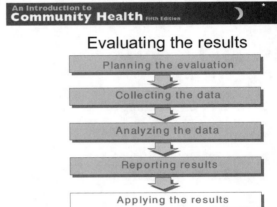

Chapter 6: The School Health Program: A Component of Community Health

Notes

Chapter Objectives

- Define coordinated school health program.
- List the ideal members of a school health team.
- Explain why a school health program is important.
- Identify the major foundations of a coordinated school health program.

Chapter Objectives

- Define written school health policies and explain their importance to the school health program.
- Explain processes for developing and implementing school health pollicies.
- List eight components of a coordinated school health program.
- Describe the role of the school health coordinator.

Notes

Chapter Objectives

- Identify those services offered as a part of school health services and explain why schools are logical places to offer such services.
- Describe three models for offering school health services.
- Explain what is meant by healthy school environment and discuss two major environments.

Chapter Objectives

- Define health education.
- Identify the seven National Health Education Standards.
- Explain how a health educator could locate credible health education curricula.
- Identify and briefly explain four issues that are faced by school health advocates.

Introduction

- The school health program is an important component of community health because every citizen must pass through this institution.

Notes

_____

An Introduction to
Community Health Fifth Edition

Definition

- Coordinated school health program
  - An organized set of policies, procedures, and activities designed to protect, promote, and improve the health and well-being of students and staff, thus improving the student's ability to learn.
- Components
  - School health education
  - Health services
  - School environment
  - Counseling
  - Psychological and social services
  - Physical education
  - School nutrition
  - Family and community
  - Health promotion

An Introduction to
Community Health Fifth Edition

Coordinated School Health Program

An Introduction to
Community Health Fifth Edition

School Health Team

Students	Parents
Teachers	Administrators
Medical personnel	Maintenance workers
Social workers	Food service workers
Counseling	Personnel

Primary role is to provide coordination of the various component of the coordinated school health program.

Notes

School Health Team

- School nurse
  - Providing direct health care to students and staff
  - Providing leadership for the provision of health services
  - Promoting a healthy school environment
  - Promoting health
  - Serving in a leadership role for health policies and programs
  - Serving as a liaison between school personnel, family, community, and health care providers

School Health Team

- Teacher's role
  - Instruction
  - Services
  - School living
  - Coordination

Need for School Health

- Health of children and their learning are reciprocally related.
  - Unhealthy child has a difficult time learning.
  - Unhealthy child can be disruptive to others.
  - School programs included in *Healthy People 2010*.
  - Not a cure-all.

Notes

School Program Foundations

Support of school administration	Well-organized school health council	Written school health policies

School Health Policies

- Written statements that provide a framework to guide
- Describe the nature of the program and procedures for its implementation
  - Development
  - Implementation
  - Monitoring the status of school health policy in the United States

Comprehensive School Health Components

- Administration and Organization
- School Health Services
  - Health appraisals
  - Emergency services
  - Prevention and control of communicable diseases
- Healthful School Environment
  - Physical
  - Psychosocial
- Health Education
  - Includes all health education in the schools

Notes

_____

_____

_____

_____

_____

_____

_____

_____

_____

_____

_____

_____

_____

_____

_____

_____

_____

_____

_____

_____

_____

_____

_____

_____

_____

_____

_____

_____

_____

_____

_____

_____

_____

_____

_____

_____

_____

_____

_____

_____

_____

_____

An Introduction to
Community Health Fifth Edition

School Health Instruction

– Community health
– Consumer health
– Environmental health
– Family life
– Mental and emotional health
– Injury prevention and safety
– Nutrition
– Personal health
– Prevention and control of disease
– Substance use and abuse
– Growth and development/sexuality

An Introduction to
Community Health Fifth Edition

Concerns and Issues

• Comprehensive school health programs
  – Research shows programs work; however, they are not in place in all schools, although the need is strong.
• Controversy
  – Based on differing values and religious teachings and on differences regarding the proper implementation of the curriculum.
• School-based clinics/School linked clinics
  – Offer comprehensive health services; have met with resistance in certain communities.
• Violence in schools
  – Risk factors need to be identified.

An Introduction to
Community Health Fifth Edition

Barriers to Comprehensive School Health Education

• Lack of local administrative commitment
• Lack of adequate prepared teachers
• Lack of time in the school day/year
• Lack of money/funds
• Health education's lack of credibility as an academic subject
• Lack of community/parental support and controversial topics

Notes

_____

_____

_____

_____

_____

_____

_____

_____

_____

An Introduction to
Community Health Fifth Edition

Reducing Controversial School Health Curricula

- Implementing age-appropriate curricula
- Using acceptable teaching methods
- Gaining parent/guardian approval
- Developing a school policy that allows parents/guardians to review the curriculum being taught and have the right to remove their child if they believe it is necessary
- Implementing a school policy for handling concerns from parents
- Making sure qualified teachers teach

Chapter 7: Maternal, Infant, and Child Health

Notes

Chapter Objectives

- Define maternal, infant, and child health.
- Explain the importance of maternal, infant, and child health as indicators of a society's health.
- Define family planning and explain why it is important.
- Identify consequences of teenage pregnancies.

Chapter Objectives

- Define legalized abortion and discuss *Roe v. Wade* and the pro-life and pro-choice movements.
- Define maternal mortality rate.
- Define prenatal care and discuss reasons for the lack of prenatal care and the influence this has on pregnancy outcome.

_____
_____
_____
_____
_____
_____
_____
_____
_____
_____
_____
_____
_____
_____
_____
_____
_____
_____
_____
_____
_____
_____
_____
_____
_____
_____
_____
_____
_____
_____
_____
_____
_____
_____
_____
_____
_____
_____

An Introduction to
Community Health Fifth Edition

Chapter Objectives

- List the major factors that contribute to infant health and mortality.
- Explain the differences among infant mortality, neonatal mortality, and post-neonatal mortality.
- Identify the leading causes of childhood morbidity and mortality.

An Introduction to
Community Health Fifth Edition

Chapter Objectives

- List the immunizations required in order for a two-year-old child to be considered fully immunized.
- Explain how health insurance and health care services impact childhood health.

An Introduction to
Community Health Fifth Edition

Chapter Objectives

- Identify important governmental programs developed to improve maternal and child health.
- Briefly explain what WIC programs are and who they serve.
- Identify the major groups who are recognized as advocates for children.

_____

_____

_____

_____

_____

_____

_____

_____

_____

_____

_____

_____

_____

_____

_____

_____

_____

_____

_____

_____

_____

_____

_____

_____

_____

_____

_____

_____

_____

_____

_____

_____

_____

_____

_____

_____

_____

An Introduction to
Community Health Fifth Edition

Definition

- Maternal, infant, and child health encompasses the health of women of childbearing age from pre-pregnancy, through pregnancy, labor, and delivery, and the postpartum period and the health of the child prior to birth through adolescence.

An Introduction to
Community Health Fifth Edition

Introduction

- Maternal, infant, and child health are important to a community's health.
  - Maternal, infant, and child health heath statistics are important indicators of the effectiveness of the disease prevention and health promotion services in the community.

An Introduction to
Community Health Fifth Edition

Continued

- Examples of precursors to high mortality rates of maternal, infants, and child health:
  - Unintended pregnancies
  - Lack of prenatal care
  - Poor maternal and child nutrition
  - Maternal drug use
  - Low immunization rates
  - Poverty
  - Limited education
  - Insufficient child care
  - Lack of health care services in the community

An Introduction to
Community Health Fifth Edition

Continued

- Many risk factors can be reduced or prevented with early intervention or education programs or preventive medical services for women, infants, and children.
- Examples of prevention services:
  - Stronger medical and social services

An Introduction to
Community Health Fifth Edition

How Healthy Are We as a Nation?

- The health of a nation can be judged by the health of its youngest members.
- Disparity can be traced to differences in socioeconomic status between segments of the population.
- Among industrial nations in the world, the United States of America is ranked 28th in infant mortality.

An Introduction to
Community Health Fifth Edition

Initial Steps in Improving Maternal, Infant, and Child Health

- Children today face different threats than past decades that put their health at risk.
- The different maternal, infant, and child mortality rates of different racial groups must be examined.

An Introduction to
Community Health Fifth Edition

Definitions of Family

- The U.S. Census Bureau defines family as "a group of two people or more (one of whom is the householder) related by birth, marriage, or adoption and residing together."
- Friedman's definition states that a family is "two or more persons who are joined together by bonds of sharing and emotional closeness and who identify themselves as being part of a family."
- Community health perspective: A marriage, or having two parents, serves as an important family characteristic in relation to a child's well-being.

An Introduction to
Community Health Fifth Edition

Research on the Family

- Increased health risks for infants and children who are raised in single-parent families.
  - Adverse birth outcomes
  - Low birth weights
  - Increase of infant mortality
  - Children living in poverty

An Introduction to
Community Health Fifth Edition

Family and Reproductive Health

- Teenage pregnancy
  - Annually 900,000.
  - 90% of unmarried teenage pregnancies were unintended.
  - 55% end in birth.
  - 31% end in abortion.
  - 14% end in miscarriages.
    - Although the U.S. has seen a decrease in teenage pregnancies, the U.S. rate is still twice that of any other industrial nation, and the teen abortion rate is three times that of many other nations.

An Introduction to
Community Health Fifth Edition

- Teenage pregnancy has greater health risks:
  - More likely to divorce early
  - Less likely to receive an adequate education
  - Greater incidence of infant low birth weight and prematurity, and higher mortality rates
  - Live in poverty

An Introduction to
Community Health Fifth Edition

Teenage Pregnancy Statistics

- Every day in the United States:
  - 7,500 unintended pregnancies occur.
  - 2,500 mothers younger than 20 years of age become pregnant, with less than one-quarter intending to become pregnant.
  - 4,000 abortions are performed.
  - 2,500 babies are born to mothers who are not high school graduates.
  - 2,600 babies are born into poverty.
  - 400 babies are born to females who received late or no prenatal care.

An Introduction to
Community Health Fifth Edition

Selected Characteristics of Teenage Mothers and Mothers 20 and Over

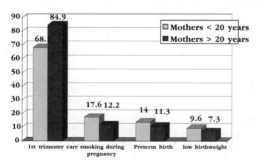

An Introduction to
Community Health Fifth Edition

Family Planning

- Process of determining the preferred number and spacing of children in one's family and choosing the appropriate means to achieve this preference.
- Nongovernment
  - Planned Parenthood Federation of America, Inc.
- Government
  - Title X
  - Broad range of acceptable family planning methods
  - Encourage family participation
  - Give priority to low-income families

An Introduction to
Community Health Fifth Edition

Abortion

- *Roe v. Wade,* 1973
  - Number of deaths from illegal abortion has declined
  - Number of legal abortion has started to decline.
- Pro-life
- Pro-choice

An Introduction to
Community Health Fifth Edition

Maternal Health

- The health of women in the childbearing years.
- Maternal mortality: The death of a woman while pregnant or within 42 days of termination of pregnancy, irrespective of the duration and site of the pregnancy, from any cause related to or aggravated by the pregnancy or its management.

Prenatal Health Care

- Fundamental to safe motherhood
  - Risk assessment
  - Treatment for medical conditions or risk reduction
  - Education
- Crucial to maternal and infant health
  - Main policy goal is to reduce low birth weight

Infant Health

- Infant's health depends upon many factors
- Infant mortality
- Infant death: Child under 1 year of age
- Infant mortality rate =

$$\frac{\text{Deaths of children under 1 yr}}{1,000 \text{ live births}}$$

Causes of Infant Mortality

- Neonatal mortality: Birth to 28 days of life
  - Premature births
  - Low birth weight
  - Birth defects

An Introduction to
Community Health Fifth Edition

Causes of Infant Mortality

- Postneonatal mortality: 28 to 365 days of life
  - Birth defects
  - Sudden infant death syndrome (SIDS)
    - Third leading cause of death of infants
    - Defined as sudden unanticipated death of an infant in whom, after examination, there is no recognized cause of death
    - Usually occurs in infants between the ages of 2 and 4 months

An Introduction to
Community Health Fifth Edition

Improving Infant Health

- Majority of birth defects attributed to environmental hazards and unhealthy behaviors of the mother during pregnancy
- Low birth weight
  - 40 times more likely to die in first year of life than healthy babies.
  - Smoking
  - Alcohol and other drugs
  - Breastfeeding

An Introduction to
Community Health Fifth Edition

Child Health

- Mortality
  - Unintentional injuries
    - Motor vehicles
  - Homicide rates
  - Suicide rates
- Morbidity
  - Unintentional injuries
  - Child abuse and neglect
  - Infectious diseases

Notes

Causes of Death Ages 1 to 14

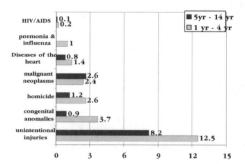

Community Programs

- 35 health programs in 16 agencies to serve the needs of our Nation's children.
- Maternal and Child Health Bureau
  - Maternal and Child Health Service Block Grant Program
  - The Healthy Start Initiative
  - The Emergency Medical Services for Children Program
  - The Abstinence Education Program

Women, Infants and Children Program

- WIC program criteria
  - Reside in the state
  - Meet the income guidelines
  - Meet the nutritional risk criteria as determined by assessment
- Providing health insurance
  - Medicaid
  - Children's Health Insurance Program (CHIP)
- Family and Medical Leave Act (FMLA)

Notes

_____

_____

_____

_____

_____

_____

_____

_____

_____

_____

_____

_____

Advocates for Children

- Children Defense Fund
- United Nations Children's Fund
- American Academy of Pediatrics

Notes

_____
_____
_____
_____
_____
_____
_____
_____
_____
_____
_____
_____
_____
_____
_____
_____
_____
_____
_____
_____
_____
_____
_____
_____
_____
_____
_____
_____
_____
_____
_____
_____
_____
_____
_____
_____
_____
_____

Chapter Objectives

- Explain why it is important for community health workers to be aware of the different health concerns of the various age groups in the United States.
- Define by age the groups of adolescents and young adults, and adults.
- Briefly describe key demographic characteristics of adolescents and young adults.

Chapter Objectives

- Explain what the Youth Risk Behavior Surveillance System (YRBSS) and the Behavioral Risk Factor Surveillance System (BRFSS) are and what type of data they generate.
- Provide a brief behavioral risk profile for adolescents, college students, and adults.

Notes

Chapter Objectives

- **Outline the health profiles for the various age groups—adolescents and young adults, and adults—listing major causes of mortality, morbidity, and risk factors for each group.**
- **Give examples of community health strategies for improving the health status of adolescents and young adults, and adults.**

Introduction

- Adolescents:15–24 years of age.
- Adults: 25–64 years of age.
- Most productive years of life: 15–64 years. Examples such as completing formal education, raising families, vocations, etc.
- Understanding age group health risks and problems:
  - Detect risks for specific target populations
  - Propose specific reduction programs

Adolescents and Young Adults

- Fall into the 15- to 24-year-old range.
- Very important to the United States because this age group is the future of our country.
- Two subgroups
  - Puberty to maturity
    - Faces hormonal changes, physical maturation, and frequent opportunities to engage in risky behavior.
  - Young adults
    - Face many physical, emotional, and educational changes (for example, completion of physical development and maturity, marriages, starting families and careers).

Adolescents and Young Adults

- Critical time period
  - This stage in life can be the most difficult due to the following:
    - Increased freedom
    - Access to health-compromising substances and experiences
    - Lifestyle challenges
  - A critical stage in developing good health knowledge and habits.

Demography

- The Number of Adolescents and Young Adults
  - Baby boomers were the largest segment of adolescents and young adults, with 21% of the population. In 2000 the number of teenagers decreased to under 14%.
- Living Arrangements
  - Many adolescents and young adults live in single-parent/guardian homes, which has contributed to the high divorce rate in this country.
- Employment Status

Young Adult Population

Employment Status

- **Proportion of overall labor force has remained constant since the 1980s.**
- **Young females participating in the workforce has increased.**
- **Unemployment rates vary significantly by race and ethnicity.**
- **Access to health care is affected by employment status.**

Health Profile: Adolescents and Young Adults

- Mortality
  - Medical advances have reduced death rate dramatically.
  - Physical threat comes primarily from behavioral activities.
- Causes
  - Motor vehicle crashes
  - Other unintentional injuries
  - Homicides
  - Suicides

Suicides

Suicide

- Third leading cause of death.
- Approximately one-sixth of ninth to twelfth graders in the United States have thought seriously about attempting suicide (16.9%).
- Suicide rates are significantly lower for females than for males. However, females attempt suicide approximately twice as often as males.

Notes

Teen Suicide Rates (YRBS, 1999)

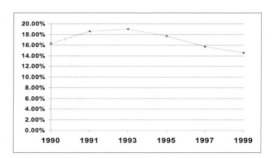

Health Profile:
Adolescents and Young Adults

- Morbidity
  - Measles
  - Sexually transmitted diseases

Causes of Morbidity

- Communicable diseases
  - Measles: Extremely severe for this age group.
    - Vaccinations
  - Sexually transmitted diseases
    - More likely than any other age group to have multiple sexual partners.
    - More likely to engage in unprotected sex.
    - More likely for young women to choose sexual partners that are older than them.

Health Behaviors and Lifestyle Choices of High School Students

- Behaviors that contribute to unintentional injury
  - Examples
    - Not using a seat belt
    - Not using a helmet during dangerous activities.
    - Riding in a car with the driver intoxicated.

Continued

- Behaviors that contribute to violence
  - Examples
    - Carrying a weapon
    - Engaging in a physical fight
    - Engaging in dating violence
    - Having being forced to have sexual intercourse
    - Engaging in school-related violence
    - Suicide ideation
    - Suicide attempts
  - Differences between the sexes

Continued

- Tobacco use
  - More than 1 million teens begin smoking.
  - Nicotine addiction.
- Alcohol and other drugs
  - Major problems dealing with alcohol and marijuana use along with other types of illicit drugs.
- Sexual behavior
  - The teenage pregnancy rates are twice as high as England, France, and Canada. The U.S. rate is nine times higher than those of the Netherlands and Japan.

Notes

_____
_____
_____
_____
_____
_____
_____
_____
_____
_____
_____
_____
_____
_____
_____
_____
_____
_____
_____
_____
_____
_____
_____
_____
_____
_____
_____
_____
_____
_____
_____
_____
_____
_____
_____

Percentage of High School Students Who Reported Sexual Risk Behaviors

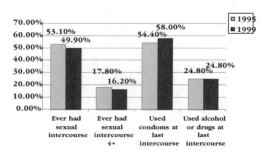

Continued

- Health behaviors and lifestyle choices
  - Lack of physical activity
  - Overweight control

Strategies for Improving the Health of Adolescents and Young Adults

- Community based
  - Involving stakeholders
- Comprehensive
- Collaborative
- Multifaceted

Notes

Health Profile:
Adults

- 25 to 64 years old
- Represents about half the U.S. population

Health Profile:
Adults

- Mortality
  - Overall death rate improving.
    - Improved health behavior and lifestyles
  - Cancer
  - Cardiovascular disease
  - Chronic disease

Death Rates (24–44 yrs; per 100,000 pop.)

Notes

Death Rates (45– 64 yrs; per 100,000 pop.)

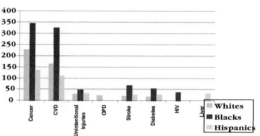

Health Profile:
Adults

- Health Behaviors and Lifestyle Choices
  - Smoking
    - Responsible for one in every six deaths.
  - Lack of exercise
  - Alcohol consumption
  - Weight

Risk Factors
for Chronic Disease

- Smoking
- Lack of exercise
- Alcohol consumption
- Body weight

An Introduction to
Community Health Fifth Edition

Risk Factors for Personal Injury

- Safety belt use
- Drinking and driving

An Introduction to
Community Health Fifth Edition

Awareness and Screening

- Hypertension
- Diabetes
- Cholesterol

An Introduction to
Community Health Fifth Edition

Strategies for Improving the Health of Adults

- Primary prevention programs
  - Exercise
  - Nutrition
- Secondary prevention
  - Clinical screening
- Tertiary prevention
  - Medication compliance

Notes

_____
_____
_____
_____
_____
_____
_____
_____
_____
_____
_____
_____
_____
_____
_____
_____
_____
_____
_____
_____
_____
_____
_____
_____
_____
_____
_____
_____
_____
_____
_____
_____
_____
_____
_____
_____
_____
_____

Chapter Objectives

- Identify the signs of an aging population.
- Define the following groups: old, young old, old old, and oldest old.
- Define the terms *aged, aging, elders, gerontology,* and *geriatrics.*
- Refute several commonly held myths about the senior population.
- Explain the meaning of an age pyramid.

Chapter Objectives

- List the factors that affect the size and age of a population.
- Define fertility and mortality rates and explain how they affect life expectancy.
- Explain the difference between support and labor-force ratios.
- Briefly outline elder abuse and neglect in the United States.

_____

_____

_____

_____

_____

_____

_____

_____

_____

_____

_____

_____

_____

_____

_____

_____

_____

_____

_____

_____

_____

_____

_____

_____

_____

_____

_____

_____

_____

_____

_____

_____

An Introduction to
Community Health Fifth Edition

Chapter Objectives

- **Describe the typical elder with regard to marital status, living arrangements, racial and ethnic background, economic status, and geographic location.**
- **Explain how four health behaviors can improve the quality of later life.**
- **Identify the six instrumental needs of elders.**

An Introduction to
Community Health Fifth Edition

Chapter Objectives

- **Briefly summarize the Older Americans Act of 1965.**
- **List the services provided for elders in most communities.**
- **Explain the difference between respite care and adult day care.**
- **Identify the four different levels of tasks with which elders need assistance.**

An Introduction to
Community Health Fifth Edition

Introduction

- The American population is growing older.
- The number of elders in America increased dramatically in the twentieth century.
- Age is and always will be a relative concept.

Notes

_____
_____
_____
_____
_____
_____
_____
_____
_____
_____
_____
_____
_____
_____
_____
_____
_____
_____
_____
_____
_____
_____
_____
_____
_____
_____
_____
_____
_____
_____
_____
_____
_____
_____

Definitions

- Aged
  - State of being old.
- Aging
  - Changes that occur as living things grow older.
- Gerontology
  - Study of aging from the broadest perspective.
- Geriatrics
  - Medical practice specializing in treatment of the aged.

Myths of Aging

- Myth
  - "After age 65, life goes steadily downhill."
- Truth
  - Any chronological age that defines old age is arbitrary. Nonetheless, many gerontologists are substituting age 85 for age 65 as the new chronological definition of old age.

Myths of Aging

- Myth
  - "Old people are all alike."
- Truth
  - There are more differences among seniors than among any other segment of the U.S. population.

Notes

_____

_____

_____

_____

_____

_____

_____

_____

_____

_____

_____

_____

_____

_____

_____

_____

_____

_____

_____

_____

_____

_____

_____

_____

_____

_____

_____

_____

_____

_____

_____

_____

_____

Myths of Aging

- Myth
  - "Old people are lonely and ignored by their families."
- Truth
  - Seniors are the least likely to be lonely of any age group, and those who live alone are likely to be in close contact, either in person or by telephone, with close friends and/or their family.

Myths of Aging

- Myth
  - "Old people are senile."
- Truth
  - Senility is the result of disease and only affects about 5% of seniors living in noninstitutional settings.

Myths of Aging

- Myth
  - "Old people have a good life."
- Truth
  - Though seniors do gain certain advantages when they retire and when their children leave home, they still face a number of concerns such as loss of loved ones, loss of health, and loss of value in society.

Myths of Aging

- Myth
  - "Most old people are sickly."
- Truth
  - Most older people do have at least one chronic health problem, but the majority of elders live active lifestyles.

Myths of Aging

- Myth
  - "Old people no longer have any sexual interest or ability."
- Truth
  - Sexual interest does not diminish with age, but there is an alteration in sexual response. Nonetheless, many seniors in reasonably good health have active and satisfying sex lives.

Myths of Aging

- Myth
  - "Most old people end up in nursing homes."
- Truth
  - Only approximately 4% of those above the age of 65 live in nursing homes. Only 1% of those aged 65 to 74 reside in such a place, though the percentage jumps to 19% for the oldest old (those 85 and older).

Myths of Aging

- Myth
  - "Older people are unproductive."
- Truth
  - Older adults are more likely to be retired, but they are very likely to be productively engaged at home and in the community.

Demography of Aging

- Size and growth
- Baby boom generation
  - Will begin to turn 65 by 2030.
  - 71 million people (one in five) will be 65 or older.
  - Population aged 85 is the fastest growing population.
  - Increasing aged and decreasing young old.
- Factors that affect population size and age
  - Fertility rates
  - Mortality rate
  - Migration and net migration

Support and Labor-Force Ratios

- Support ratio
  - Comparison between society's unproductive and productive individuals
  - Total support ratio
  - Youth support ratio
  - Elderly support ratio
- Labor-force support ratio
  - Based on the number who are actually working

_____

Demography of Aging

- **Marital status and other variables**
  - Men have shorter life expectancies, leaving women behind.
  - Men tend to marry women younger than themselves.
  - Men are more likely to remarry if they lose their spouse.
    - Statistically, this reveals that most men have spouse assistance.
  - The number of divorced elders continue to rise from the baby boomers.
    - Represents new problems.

Demography of Aging

- **Living arrangements**
  - Older people who live alone are more likely to live in poverty than elders who have spouses.
  - Nursing homes.
  - Assisted living facilities.

Demography of Aging

- **Racial and ethnic composition**
  - 2000 data
    - 84% white
    - 8% black
    - 6% Hispanic origin
    - 2% Asian/Pacific Islander
    - 1% American Indian and Alaskan Native
  - Projected 2050 data
    - 64% white
    - 16% black
    - 12% Hispanic Americans
    - 7% Asian/Pacific Islander
    - Less than 1% American Indian and Alaskan Native

Notes

_____

_____

_____

_____

_____

_____

_____

_____

_____

_____

_____

_____

_____

_____

_____

_____

_____

_____

_____

_____

_____

_____

_____

_____

_____

_____

_____

_____

_____

_____

_____

_____

_____

_____

Demography of Aging

- **Geographic distribution**
  - **One-third of elders live in the Southern states.**
- **Economic status**
  - **Has improved since 1970.**

Income Sources of Seniors

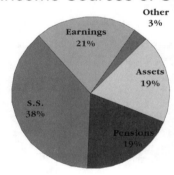

Housing Needs of Seniors

Housing

- *Older homes*
- *Homes of lower value*
- *In need of repair*
- *Less likely to have central heating and air conditioning*
- *Less likely to have a telephone*

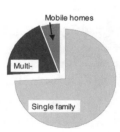

An Introduction to
Community Health Fifth Edition

Health Profile of Elders

- Mortality
- Morbidity
  - Chronic conditions
    - Hypertension, arthritis, heart disease, diabetes, emphysema
  - Impairments
    - Sensory and motor

An Introduction to
Community Health Fifth Edition

Health Behaviors

- Less likely to
  - Consume large amounts of alcohol
  - Smoke cigarettes
  - Be overweight or obese
- When compared with younger counterparts.

An Introduction to
Community Health Fifth Edition

Neglect and Abuse

- Female elders are abused at a higher rate than men.
- Elders 80 years and older are abused or neglected at two to three times the rate of their proportion of the elderly population.
- In 90% of abuse cases the perpetrator is a family member, and two-thirds of the perpetrators are adult children or spouses.
- Victims of self-neglect are usually depressed, confused, or extremely frail.

An Introduction to
Community Health Fifth Edition

Instrumental Needs of Elders

- **Income**
- **Housing**
- **Personal care**
- **Health care**

An Introduction to
Community Health Fifth Edition

Transportation Concerns of Seniors

- Important to remain independent
- Solutions to transportation problems
  - Fare reductions
  - Subsidies to mass transit
  - Subsidies for taxis
  - Funds to assist centers in purchasing equipped vehicles

An Introduction to
Community Health Fifth Edition

Community Facilities & Services

- Meal service
  - Programs such as Meals on Wheels and congregate meals
- Homemaker service
  - Enables elderly to remain in their own homes
- Chore and home maintenance service
- Visitor service

Notes

_____

_____

_____

_____

_____

_____

_____

_____

_____

_____

Community Facilities & Services

- Adult day care
  - Provides care for seniors left alone all day
- Respite care
- Home health care
- Senior centers
- Other services

Chapter 10: Community Health and Minorities

Notes

_____

_____

_____

_____

_____

_____

_____

_____

_____

_____

_____

_____

_____

_____

_____

_____

_____

_____

_____

_____

_____

_____

_____

_____

_____

_____

_____

_____

_____

_____

_____

_____

_____

_____

_____

_____

_____

_____

_____

_____

Chapter Objectives

- Explain the concept of diversity as it describes the American people.
- Explain the impact of a more diverse population in the United States as it relates to community health efforts.
- Explain the importance of the 1985 landmark report *The Secretary's Task Force on Black and Minority Health*.

Chapter Objectives

- List the racial and ethnic categories currently used by the U.S. government in statistical activities and program administration reporting.
- List some limitations related to collecting racial and ethnic health data.
- Identify some of the sociodemographic and socioeconomic characteristics of minority groups in the United States.

Notes

Chapter Objectives

- List some of the beliefs and values of minority groups in the United States.
- List and describe the six priority areas of the Race and Health Initiative.
- Define socioeconomic gradient and provide an example as it relates to minority health.

Chapter Objectives

- Define cultural sensitivity and cultural competence and define the importance of each related to minority community health.
- Identify the three kinds of power associated with empowerment and explain the importance of each related to minority community health.

Overview of Diversity

- The strength and greatness of America lies in the diversity of its people.
- The failure to understand and appreciate diversity can have serious implications not only for race relations, but also when it comes to improving the nation's health.
  - President's Initiative on Race
  - Majority
  - Minorities

Notes

_____

_____

_____

_____

_____

_____

_____

_____

_____

_____

_____

_____

_____

_____

_____

_____

_____

_____

_____

_____

_____

_____

_____

_____

_____

_____

_____

_____

_____

_____

_____

_____

_____

_____

_____

_____

Documents

- *The Secretary's Task Force Report on Black and Minority Health*
- *Healthy People 2000* and *2010*
- *Initiative to Eliminate Racial and Ethnic Minorities in Health*
  - Prevent disease
  - Promote health
  - Delivering care to racial and ethnic minority communities

Racial and Ethnic Classifications

- U.S. Office of Management and Budget
  - Operationalizes race and ethnicity
- 1997 classification standards expanded race from four to five categories

Health Data Sources and Their Limitations

- Gaps in the information system
- Bias analysis
- Self-reported data
- Reliability

An Introduction to
Community Health Fifth Edition

Black Americans

- Second largest minority group
- Socioeconomic characteristics
  - Low average education level
  - Lowest median income
- Vital statistics
  - 34.5 million; 12.1% of population

An Introduction to
Community Health Fifth Edition

Black Americans

- Major community health problems
  - Infant mortality
  - Sickle cell disease
  - HIV/AIDS
  - Violent deaths

An Introduction to
Community Health Fifth Edition

Americans of Hispanic Origin

- Vital statistics
  - 35.3 million; 12.5% of population
  - Low average education level
  - Low average income
- Religious beliefs
  - Role of God

Notes

_____

_____

_____

_____

_____

_____

_____

_____

_____

_____

_____

_____

_____

_____

_____

_____

_____

_____

_____

_____

_____

_____

_____

_____

_____

_____

_____

_____

_____

_____

_____

_____

_____

_____

_____

_____

_____

_____

Asian/Pacific Islanders

- Vital statistics
  - 10.5 million; 3.7% of the population
  - Fastest growing ethnic population in the U.S.
  - High school completion and income are highest among the ethnic groups
- Consists of two distinct groups (Asian Americans and Pacific Islanders)

Native Americans and Alaskan Natives

- Demographic characteristics
  - 2.5 million; nearly 1% of the population
- Vital statistics
  - Economically disadvantaged
  - Poor health status
  - Poverty rate of 25.9%
  - Low high school completion rate

Native Americans

- Health care: Indian Health Service
  - Established in 1954; first federal agency to address health
  - #1 health problem: Alcohol abuse
  - Intentional and unintentional injuries

Notes

Indian Health Service

- Four goals for success:
  - Assist Indian tribes in developing health programs.
  - Facilitate and assist Indian tribes in coordinating health resources.
  - Provide comprehensive health care services.
  - Serve as a Federal advocate.

U.S. Population Estimates 2000

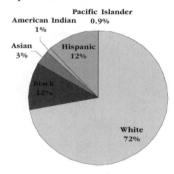

U.S. Population 2050 projected

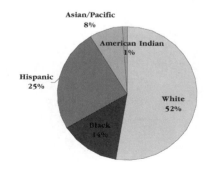

Estimated Median Household Income

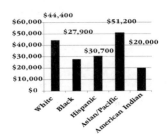

Estimated Poverty Rates

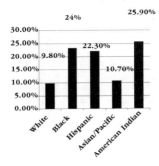

Refugees: New Immigrants

- Refugees: People who flee their homes from danger.
- Immigrants: Migrate from other countries to set up residence in another country.
- Aliens: People who were not born in a particular country.
- Illegal aliens: Entered a country without permission.
- Special concerns
  - Poor
  - Lower levels of education
  - Few work skills
  - Serious health problems

An Introduction to
Community Health Fifth Edition

Race and Health Initiative

- Infant mortality
- Cancer screening and management
- Cardiovascular disease
- Diabetes
- HIV/AIDS
- Adult and child immunizations
  - *Healthy People 2010*

An Introduction to
Community Health Fifth Edition

Socioeconomic Status & Racial and Ethnic Disparities in Health

- Indirect causal associations
  - Level of education
  - Level of income
  - Poverty
- Group living circumstances

An Introduction to
Community Health Fifth Edition

Community Health Strategies for Achieving Equity in Minority Health

- Cultural Competence
  - A set of congruent behaviors, attitudes, and policies that come together in a system, agency, or among professionals that enables effective work in cross-cultural situations.
- Empowering the Self and the Community
  - Social power
  - Political power
  - Psychological power

Notes

_____

_____

_____

_____

_____

_____

_____

_____

_____

_____

_____

_____

_____

_____

_____

_____

_____

_____

_____

_____

_____

_____

_____

_____

_____

_____

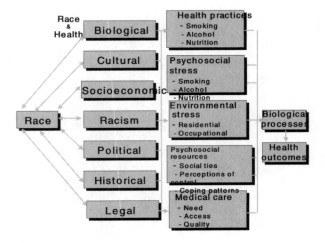

An Introduction to
Community Health Fifth Edition

Ten Principles Related to Cultural Competencies

1. Have an understanding of race, ethnicity, and power.
2. Understand historical factors.
3. Understand psychosocial stressors.
4. Understand cultural differences.
5. Understand minority client within the family life cycle and in an intergenerational conceptual framework.
6. Know the difference between culturally acceptable behaviors and psychopathological characteristics.
7. Understand indigenous healing practices.
8. Understand cultural beliefs of health.
9. Understand health resources available.
10. Understand public health policies.

Chapter 11: Community Mental Health

Notes

Chapter Objectives

- Define mental health and mental disorders.
- Explain what is meant by the DSM-IV-R.
- Identify the major causes of mental disorders.
- Explain why mental health is one of the major community health problems in the United States.

Chapter Objectives

- Define stress and explain its relationship to physical and mental health.
- Briefly trace the history of mental health care in America, highlighting the major changes both before and after World War II.
- Define the term *deinstitutionalization* and list and discuss the propelling forces that brought it about.

Notes

_____

_____

_____

_____

_____

_____

_____

_____

_____

_____

_____

_____

_____

_____

_____

_____

_____

_____

_____

_____

_____

_____

_____

_____

_____

_____

_____

_____

_____

_____

_____

_____

_____

_____

_____

_____

_____

_____

_____

An Introduction to
Community Health Fifth Edition

Chapter Objectives

- Describe the movement toward community mental health centers.
- Explain what is meant by Community Support Program and list some of the services provided by successful programs.
- Identify the major mental and physical problems of the homeless.
- Define primary, secondary, and tertiary prevention as they relate to mental health care services.

An Introduction to
Community Health Fifth Edition

Chapter Objectives

- **List and briefly describe the three basic approaches to treatment for mental disorders.**
- **Define self-help groups, give examples, and explain how they are helpful to their members.**
- **Explain the purpose of the Substance Abuse and Mental Health Services Administration.**

An Introduction to
Community Health Fifth Edition

Chapter Objectives

- **Define what is meant by behavioral health care services.**
- **Define evidence-based practices in behavioral health interventions.**
- **Explain what is at issue when the term _parity in health care services_ is used in reference to health care services for the mentally ill.**

Notes

Introduction

- Mental illness: Diagnosable mental disorders.
- Mental illness is a major community health issue.
  - 22% to 23% (44 million) of American adults affected
  - 6% have addictive behaviors
  - 3% have both mental and addictive disorders
  - Small portion of those diagnosed receive treatment

Community Mental Health

- Mental health
  - State of successful performance of mental function, resulting in productive activities, fulfilling relationships with other people, and the ability to adapt to change and to cope with adversity.

Community Mental Health

- Characteristics
  - Function under adversity
  - Change or adapt to changes around them
  - Maintain control over their tension and anxiety
  - Find more satisfaction in giving than receiving
  - Show consideration for others
  - Curb hate and guilt
  - Love others

Notes

_____

_____

_____

_____

_____

_____

_____

_____

_____

_____

_____

_____

_____

_____

_____

_____

_____

_____

_____

_____

_____

_____

_____

_____

_____

_____

_____

_____

_____

_____

_____

_____

_____

_____

_____

_____

_____

_____

_____

_____

_____

_____

_____

_____

Mental Illness

- Mental disorders
  - Health conditions that are characterized by alterations in thinking, mood, or behavior associated with distress and/or impaired functioning.
- Classification
  - DSM-IV (*Diagnostic and Statistical Manual of Mental Disorders,* 4th edition)
  - Type of onset
  - Severity

Diagnostic Categories of Mental Disorders

- Disorders usually first evident in infancy, childhood, or adolescence
  - Mental retardation, attention-deficit hyperactivity disorder
- Organic mental disorders
  - Alzheimer's disease, dementia associated with alcoholism or chronic drug use
- Psychoactive substance use disorders
  - Alcohol, nicotine, cocaine, or other drug dependence
- Schizophrenia
  - Paranoid schizophrenia
- Delusional disorder
  - Persecutory delusional disorder

Diagnostic Categories of Mental Disorders

- Miscellaneous psychotic disorders
  - Brief reactive psychosis
- Mood disorders
  - Major depression; bipolar disorder
- Anxiety disorders
  - Panic disorders, obsessive compulsive disorder, post-traumatic stress disorder
- Somatoform disorders
  - Conversion disorder; hypochondriasis
- Dissociative disorders
  - Multiple personality disorders
- Sexual disorders
  - Paraphilias; sexual dysfunction

Notes

Diagnostic Categories
of Mental Disorders

- Sleep disorders
  - Insomnia disorder; dream anxiety disorder
- Impulse control disorders
  - Kleptomania; pathological gambling
- Adjustment disorders
  - Anxious mood; withdrawal
- Personality disorders
  - Avoidant, dependent, obsessive

Origins and Causes
of Mental Disorders

- Deficiency at birth
- Physical impairment
- Idiopathic
- Environmental
- Inherited (genetic)
- Maternal exposure
  - Physical agents
  - Chemical agents
  - Biological agents

Mental Illness In America

- Statistical indicators
  - Between 15.4% of adults have had at least one episode of a mental disorder in the past 30 days.
  - About 35% of the population aged 15 to 54 have had a mental disorder.

_____

_____

_____

_____

_____

_____

_____

_____

_____

_____

_____

_____

_____

_____

_____

_____

_____

_____

_____

_____

_____

_____

_____

_____

_____

_____

_____

_____

_____

_____

_____

_____

_____

_____

_____

_____

An Introduction to
Community Health Fifth Edition

Mental Illness in America

- Social indicators
  - Homicides: Second leading cause of death in the 15- to 24-year age group.
  - Suicides: Third leading cause of death in the 15- to 24-year age group.
  - There are nearly 30,000 suicides each year.
  - High rate of divorce.
  - Current widespread abuse of alcohol and tobacco.

An Introduction to
Community Health Fifth Edition

Mental Illness in America

- Stress
  - One's psychological and physiological response to stressors
  - General Adaptation Syndrome (GAS)
    - Alarm reaction
    - Resistance
    - Exhaustion
  - Diseases of adaptation
  - Fight or flight reaction

An Introduction to
Community Health Fifth Edition

General Adaptation Syndrome

Perceived stressor	Alarm reaction	Stage of resistance	Stage of exhaustion
	Body is modified to defend against the stressor	Arousal remains high, as body tries to defend against & adapt to the stressor.	Resources are very limited; ability to resist may collapse

_____

An Introduction to
Community Health Fifth Edition

Psychophysiological Disorders Associated with Stress

- **Asthma**
- **Cancer**
- **Depression**
- **Dysmenorrhea**
- **Exhaustion**
- **Hypertension**

- **Gastrointestinal problems**
- **Coronary heart disease**
- **Inflammatory bowel disease**
- **Skin disorders**
- **Headaches**

An Introduction to
Community Health Fifth Edition

History of Mental Care in America

- Colonial America
- Nineteenth century
  - Moral Treatment Era
- State-supported hospitals
  - Dorothea Dix (1802-1897)
  - Number of state hospitals grew rapidly during last 25 years of nineteenth century

An Introduction to
Community Health Fifth Edition

History of Mental Care in America

- 1900–1920: Mental Hygiene Movement
  - Early identification and treatment (acute care) for those with mental illness to preclude the use of state hospitals
  - Dr. Adolf Meyer (1866–1950)
  - Clifford Beers (1876–1943)
- Mental health in the 1920s and 1930s
  - Conditions in state mental hospitals continued to decline
  - First mention of deinstitutionalization

Notes

An Introduction to
Community Health Fifth Edition

History of Mental Care in America

- World War II
  - State hospitals continued to deteriorate
  - 15 million men were rejected from service for mental retardation and mental illness
  - Virtually all psychiatrists were drafted
  - New methods and drugs were developed
- National Mental Health Act of of 1946
  - National Institute of Mental Health was established
  - People began to realize the plight of the state mental hospitals

An Introduction to
Community Health Fifth Edition

History of Mental Care in America

- 1950s: Era of Deinstitutionalization
  - Economics
  - Idealism
  - Legal considerations
  - Antipsychotic drugs

An Introduction to
Community Health Fifth Edition

History of Mental Care in America

- Mental health care in the 1960s
  - Community Mental Health Centers Act: 1963
  - Medicare and Medicaid: 1966
  - Transinstituionalized

An Introduction to
Community Health Fifth Edition

History of Mental Care
in America

- Mental health care in the 1970s and 1980s
  - Recognition of the failure of CMHCs to meet the needs of the deinstitutionalized mentally ill
  - Initiation of Community Support Programs to promote recovery in persons with serious and persistent mental disorders

An Introduction to
Community Health Fifth Edition

History of Mental Care
in America

- Mental health care in the 1990s
  - We were still dealing with the legacy of deinstitutionalization: homeless people with mental disorders
  - Continued absence of a comprehensive, coordinated system
  - Broadening access to treatment
- Problems of homelessness
  - Mental health problems
  - Physical health problems

An Introduction to
Community Health Fifth Edition

Meeting the Needs
of the Mentally Ill

- Prevention
  - Primary prevention: Efforts aimed at forestalling the onset of mental illness
  - Secondary prevention: Reducing the prevalence by shortening episodes
  - Tertiary prevention: Treatment, and rehabilitation to ameliorate the illness and prevent further problems for the individual and the community
- Prevention services

Notes

_____

_____

_____

_____

_____

_____

_____

_____

_____

_____

_____

_____

_____

_____

_____

_____

_____

_____

_____

_____

_____

_____

_____

_____

_____

_____

_____

_____

_____

_____

_____

_____

_____

_____

_____

_____

_____

Meeting the Needs of the Mentally Ill

- Treatment approaches
  - Goals
    - Reduce symptoms
    - Improve personal and social functioning
    - Develop and strengthen coping skills
    - Promote behaviors that improve life
  - Psychotherapy
  - Psychopharmacology
  - Self-help support groups

Nongovernmental Agencies

- National Alliance for the Mentally Ill
  - Established in 1979
  - 856 affiliates and more than 20,000 member families
  - Believe only biologically grounded treatment approaches are relevant
- Alcoholics Anonymous

Federal Agencies

- U.S. Public Health Service, SAMHSA
  - The Center for Substance Abuse Treatment
  - The Center for Substance Abuse Prevention
  - Center for Mental Health Services

An Introduction to
Community Health Fifth Edition

Future Challenges

- Managed Care Organizations (MCOs)
  - Evidenced-based medicine
  - Cost containment
  - "Behavioral health care services," MBHOs
- Parity issue
  - 1996 Mental Health Parity Act
  - There is still not full parity in health care coverage between general health care services and mental (behavioral) health care services

Chapter 12: Alcohol, Tobacco, and Other Drugs: A Community Concern

Notes

_____

_____

_____

_____

_____

_____

_____

_____

_____

_____

_____

_____

_____

_____

_____

_____

_____

_____

_____

_____

_____

_____

_____

_____

_____

_____

_____

_____

_____

_____

_____

_____

_____

_____

_____

_____

Chapter Objectives

- Identify personal and community consequences of alcohol and other drug abuse.
- Describe the trends of alcohol and other drug use by high school students.
- Define drug use, misuse, and abuse.
- Define drug dependence.

Chapter Objectives

- List and discuss the risk factors for the abuse of alcohol and other drugs.
- Explain why alcohol is considered the number 1 drug abuse problem in America.
- Describe the health risks of cigarette smoking.

An Introduction to
Community Health Fifth Edition

Chapter Objectives

- Define the terms *over-the-counter* and *prescription drugs* and explain the purpose of these drugs and how they are regulated.
- Define the terms *controlled substances* and *illicit (illegal) drugs* and provide examples.
- Characterize recent trends in the prevalence of drug use among American high school seniors.

An Introduction to
Community Health Fifth Edition

Chapter Objectives

- List and explain four elements of drug abuse prevention and control.
- Give an example of primary, secondary, and tertiary prevention activities in drug abuse prevention and control programs.
- Summarize the federal government's drug abuse control efforts.

An Introduction to
Community Health Fifth Edition

Chapter Objectives

- List and describe some community and school drug abuse prevention programs.
- List the five components of a typical workplace substance abuse prevention program.
- Name some voluntary health agencies and self-help support groups involved in the prevention, control, and treatment of alcohol, tobacco, and other drug abuse.

Notes

Introduction

- Scope of the problem
- $246–$414 billion annual economic loss

Drug	Estimated Deaths	Costs
Alcohol	100,000	$166 billion
Tobacco	430,000	$138 billion
Illicit drugs	16,000	$110 billion
Total	546,000	$414 billion

Continued

- Marijuana used by 21.6% of high school seniors in 2003, compared with 2002 data showing 11.9% of high school seniors using marijuana
- New emerging drugs: Vicodin and OxyContin
- Personal consequences
- Community consequences

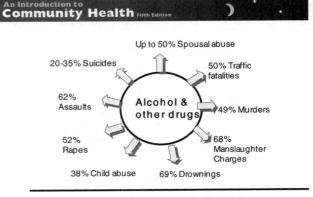

Health Concerns Associated with Alcohol Use

Notes

Definitions

- Drug
  - Substance other than food that, when taken in small quantities, alters one's physical, mental, or emotional state
- Psychoactive drug
  - Alters sensory perceptions, mood, thought process, or behavior
- Drug misuse
  - Inappropriate use of prescription or nonprescription drugs

Definitions

- Drug abuse
  - Taking of a drug for non-medically approved purposes.
  - Continued use of a legal drug with the knowledge that it is hazardous to one's health (e.g., cigarette smoking).
- Drug dependence
  - When one believes that a particular drug is necessary for normal functioning.

Factors That Contribute to Substance Abuse

- Risk factors: Factors that increase the probability of drug use
- Protective risk factors: Factors that decrease the probability of drug use
- Inherited risk factors: Genetic and biological risk factors
- Environmental risk factors
  - Personal
  - Home and family
  - School and peer group factors
  - Sociocultural aspects of one's environment

An Introduction to
Community Health Fifth Edition

Types of Drugs

- Legal (licit): Alcohol, nicotine, nonprescription drugs, and prescription drugs.
- Illegal (illicit): Stimulants, depressants, narcotics, hallucinogens, marijuana, and other drugs

An Introduction to
Community Health Fifth Edition

Types of Legal Drugs Abused

- Alcohol
  - Number 1 drug problem in America.
  - 76.6% of high school seniors have used alcohol.
  - 40% of college students report having 5 or more drinks in a row at least once in the past 2 years.
- Binge drinking
- Problem drinkers
- Alcoholism
- Blood alcohol concentration (BAC)

An Introduction to
Community Health Fifth Edition

Continued

- Alcohol contributes to the following community problems:
  - 50% of spouse abuse
  - 49% of murders
  - 62% of assaults
  - 52% of rapes
  - 38% of child abuse cases
  - 20% to 35% of suicides

Notes

_____

Types of Legal Drugs Abused

- Nicotine
  - *Use occurs in the form of cigarette, cigar, and pipe smoking, chewing tobacco, and snuff*
  - *24.4% of high school seniors smoke cigarettes daily*
  - *435,000 deaths each year*
  - *$138 billion economic cost*

•Environmental tobacco smoke (ETS)
•Spit tobacco

Types of Legal Drugs Abused

- Food and Drug Administration (FDA)
- Over-the-counter (OTC) drugs
  - Can be purchased without a doctor's prescription
- Prescription drugs
  - Require a physician's written instructions
  - Usually stronger than over-the-counter drugs

Types of Illicit Drugs Abused

- Marijuana
  - Most abused illicit drug
  - Amotivational syndrome
- Narcotics: Opium, morphine, and heroin
  - Narcotics numb the senses and reduce pain.
  - Produce tolerance and physical dependence.
  - Injection users are at high risk for becoming infected with HIV.

An Introduction to
Community Health Fifth Edition

Types of Illicit Drugs Abused

- Cocaine
  - Potent stimulant
  - 2 million Americans used in last 30 days
- Hallucinogens: Synesthesia
  - LSD
  - Mescaline
  - Psilocybin

An Introduction to
Community Health Fifth Edition

Types of Illicit Drugs Abused

- Stimulants
  - Amphetamine
  - Methamphetamine
  - Methcathinone
- Depressants
  - Barbiturates
  - Benzodiazepines
  - Methaqualone

An Introduction to
Community Health Fifth Edition

Types of Illicit Drugs Abused

- Designer drugs
  - Rohypnol and related chemicals
  - MDMA and related compounds
  - PCP and related chemicals
- Anabolic drugs
- Inhalants

_____

An Introduction to
Community Health Fifth Edition

Prevention and Control of Drug Abuse

- Primary
  - Aimed at those who have never used drugs; goal is to prevent or forestall the initiation of drug use
- Secondary
  - Seek to reach those who have begun drug use but are not chronic drug abusers
- Tertiary
  - Designed to provide treatment for abuse and aftercare

An Introduction to
Community Health Fifth Edition

Elements of Prevention

- Drug use education
- Treatment
- Public policy
- Law enforcement

Smokefree Indiana

An Introduction to
Community Health Fifth Edition

Official Agencies and Programs

- $19.2 billion 2001 federal budget
- Goals
  - Stopping drug use before it starts
  - Healing America's drug users
  - Disrupting the drug market
- Department of Justice
  - Law enforcement, prisons, and other aspects of the justice system
  - Drug Enforcement Agency
    - Lead governmental agency on drugs
  - Federal Bureau of Investigation (FBI)
  - Immigration and Naturalization Service

Notes

_____

_____

_____

_____

_____

_____

_____

_____

_____

_____

_____

_____

_____

_____

_____

_____

_____

_____

_____

_____

_____

_____

_____

_____

_____

_____

_____

_____

_____

_____

_____

_____

_____

_____

_____

Official Agencies and Programs

- Department of Health and Human Services
  - Education, automatic protection, and regulation
  - Rapid diagnosis and intervention with treatment
  - Substance abuse and mental health services
  - National Institute on Drug Abuse
- Department of Treasury
  - U.S. Customs Service
  - Internal Revenue Service (IRS)
  - Bureau of Alcohol, Tobacco, Firearms and Explosives (ATF)

Official Agencies and Programs

- Substance Abuse and Mental Health Services Administration (SAMSHA)
- National Institute of Drug Abuse (NIDA)
  - Lead federal research agency
- Department of Education (DE)
  - Programs for drug-free schools
- Food and Drug Administration (FDA)
  - Federal regulatory agency for legal drugs

New Federal Agency

- Department of Homeland Security
  - Founded by President George W. Bush.
  - Resulted from the attacks on the World Trade Center and the Pentagon on September 11, 2001.
  - Receives the third largest amount of funding from the national drug control budget.

Notes

_____
_____
_____
_____
_____
_____
_____
_____
_____
_____
_____
_____
_____
_____
_____
_____
_____
_____
_____
_____
_____
_____
_____
_____
_____
_____
_____
_____
_____
_____
_____
_____
_____
_____
_____
_____
_____

Official Agencies and Programs

- State government
  - Influences the outcome of drug wars through advocacy, administrative aid, and legislation
- Regional coordination offices
  - Provide a link between state and local efforts
- Local agencies and programs
  - Local coordination councils
  - Prevention through education
  - Intervention and treatment
  - Law enforcement

Nongovernmental Drug Prevention and Control

- Community-based drug education.
  - Six key features
    - A comprehensive strategy
    - An indirect approach to drug abuse prevention
    - The goal of empowering youth
    - A participatory approach
    - A culture-sensitive orientation
    - Highly structured activities
- School-based drug education
  - Student assistance programs (SAPs)
  - Peer counseling programs.
- Workplace-based drug education
  - Employee Assistance Programs (EAPs)

Voluntary Health Agencies

- Mothers Against Drunk Drivers
- Students Against Drunk Drivers
- Alcoholics Anonymous
- Narcotics Anonymous
- American Cancer Society

Chapter 13: Health Care System: Structure

Notes

Chapter Objectives

- Define the term *health care system*.
- Trace the history of health care delivery in the United States from the mid-nineteenth century to the present.
- Discuss and explain the concept of the spectrum of health care delivery.
- List and describe the different levels of medical practice.

Chapter Objectives

- Distinguish between the different kinds of health care, including public health practice, medical practice, long-term practice, and end-of-life practice.
- List and characterize the various groups of health care providers.
- Explain the differences among allopathic, osteopathic, and nonallopathic providers.
- Define complementary and alternative medicine.

Notes

_____

_____

_____

_____

_____

_____

_____

_____

_____

_____

_____

_____

_____

_____

_____

_____

_____

_____

_____

_____

_____

_____

_____

_____

_____

_____

_____

_____

_____

_____

_____

_____

_____

_____

_____

Chapter Objectives

- **Explain why there is a need for health care providers.**
- **Prepare a list of the different types of facilities in which health care is delivered.**
- **Explain the differences among private, public, and voluntary hospitals.**
- **Explain the concept behind ambulatory care facilities.**

Chapter Objectives

- **Briefly discuss the options for long-term care.**
- **Explain what the Joint Commission on Accreditation of Healthcare Organizations (JCAHO) does.**

Health Care System: Structure

- American delivery system
  - No national health care system
  - Variety of providers
  - Variety of settings
- Concerns
  - Informal cooperation of providers
  - Disease treatment vs. health care
  - Conglomeration vs. system

_____

_____

_____

_____

_____

_____

_____

_____

_____

_____

_____

_____

_____

_____

_____

_____

_____

_____

_____

_____

_____

_____

_____

_____

_____

_____

_____

_____

_____

_____

_____

_____

_____

_____

An Introduction to
Community Health Fifth Edition

Brief History of U.S. Health Care

An Introduction to
Community Health Fifth Edition

Brief History of U.S. Health Care

Timeline

1850   1997

An Introduction to
Community Health Fifth Edition

Brief History of U.S. Health Care

Before 1850: Medical treatment occurred in home

1850   1997

Notes

_____
_____
_____
_____
_____
_____
_____
_____
_____
_____
_____
_____
_____
_____
_____
_____
_____
_____
_____
_____
_____
_____
_____
_____
_____
_____
_____
_____
_____
_____
_____
_____
_____

An Introduction to
Community Health Fifth Edition

Brief History of U.S. Health Care

Treatment moved to physicians' offices and hospitals

Home

1850	1900	1997

An Introduction to
Community Health Fifth Edition

Brief History of U.S. Health Care

1st Insurance

Hospitals

Home

1850	1911	1997

An Introduction to
Community Health Fifth Edition

Brief History of U.S. Health Care

3.9% of GDP spent on health care

1st Insurance

Hospitals

Home

1850	1911	1929	1997

Notes

_____

_____

_____

_____

_____

_____

_____

_____

_____

_____

_____

_____

_____

_____

_____

_____

_____

_____

_____

_____

_____

_____

_____

_____

_____

_____

_____

_____

_____

_____

_____

_____

_____

_____

_____

_____

Brief History of U.S. Health Care

Age of Medicine
NIH established
Hill-Burton Act

1st Insurance

Hospitals

Home

2.9% GDP

1850   1911   **1930 – 1950**   1997

Brief History of U.S. Health Care

Medicare & Medicaid

1st Insurance

Hospitals   Age of Medicine

Home

2.9% GDP

1850   1911   1930   1950   **1965**   1997

Brief History of U.S. Health Care

Cost Containment
- Health Systems Planning
- Health Maintenance Organization Act

1st Insurance

Hospitals   Age of Medicine

Home   Medicare &
Medicaid

2.9% GDP

1850   1911   1930   1950   1965   **1970s**   1997

Notes

_____

_____

_____

_____

_____

_____

_____

_____

_____

_____

_____

_____

_____

_____

_____

_____

_____

_____

_____

_____

_____

_____

_____

_____

_____

_____

_____

_____

_____

_____

_____

_____

_____

_____

_____

An Introduction to
Community Health Fifth Edition

Brief History of U.S. Health Care

American Health
Security Act of 1993

Cost Containment

1st Insurance

Hospitals   Age of Medicine

Home   Medicare &
               Medicaid
2.9% GDP

1850   1911 1930   1950   1965 1970s **1980s** 1997

An Introduction to
Community Health Fifth Edition

Brief History of U.S. Health Care

14% GDP,
managed care

Cost Containment

1st Insurance

Age of Medicine

Home   Medicare &   Increased
               Medicaid
2.9% GDP

1850   1911 1930   1950   1965 1970 1980 **1992**

An Introduction to
Community Health Fifth Edition

Major Concerns
in the United States

1. Medical care cost
2. Drug abuse
3. Budget deficit
4. Crime
5. Unemployment
6. AIDS

Notes

_____
_____
_____
_____
_____
_____
_____
_____
_____
_____
_____
_____
_____
_____
_____
_____
_____
_____
_____
_____
_____
_____
_____
_____
_____
_____
_____
_____
_____
_____
_____
_____
_____
_____
_____
_____

Health Care Spending
(Select countries: 1960 & 1997)

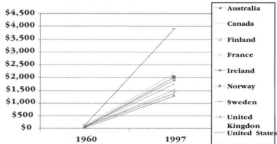

Legend: Australia, Canada, Finland, France, Ireland, Norway, Sweden, United Kingdon, United States

Spectrum of Health Care Delivery

- Spectrum of health care: Refers to the types of health care provided
- Public health practice
  - Education is primary component.
- Medical practice
  - Primary
  - Secondary
    - Acute
    - Subacute
  - Tertiary

Spectrum of Health Care Delivery

- Long-term practice
  - Restorative care
  - Long-term care
- End-of-life practice
  - Care provided to those who have less than six months left to live
  - Hospice service

An Introduction to
Community Health Fifth Edition

Public Health Practice

- Education
  - Provides information
  - Empowers
  - Motivates
  - Practice aimed at prevention
- Settings
  - Governmental health agencies
  - Voluntary health agencies
  - Social services agencies
  - Schools
  - Business and industry

An Introduction to
Community Health Fifth Edition

Primary Medical Care

- **Front line**
- **Education**
- **Promotion of nutrition**
- **Safe water and sanitation**
- **Maternal and child health care**
- **Immunization**
- **Prevention and control of endemic disease**
- **Treatment of common diseases and injuries**
- **Provide essential drugs**

An Introduction to
Community Health Fifth Edition

Secondary Medical Care

- Specialized care
  - *Provided by physicians*
  - *Hospital or outpatient*
  - *Acute care: Short term*
  - *Subacute: Provides specialty services*
  - *Emergency care*

An Introduction to
Community Health Fifth Edition

Tertiary Medical Care

- **Highly specialized and technological**
- **For those with unusual or complex conditions**
- **Specialized hospitals**
- **Academic health centers**
- **Types of illnesses: AIDS, cancer, and heart disease, and surgery**

An Introduction to
Community Health Fifth Edition

Long-Term Practice

- **Restorative care**
  - **Health care provided to patients after surgery or other forms of treatment**
- **Long-term care**
  - **Health care provided to patients with chronic illness**

An Introduction to
Community Health Fifth Edition

End-of Life Practice

- Health care provided shortly before death
- Hospice care
  - Support care services that provide holistic care for dying persons, their families, and loved ones

Health Care Providers

- Over 200 different careers in the health care industry
- Five different categories
  - Independent providers
  - Limited care providers
  - Nurses
  - Allied health care professionals
  - Public health professionals

Health Care Providers

- Independent providers
  - Allopathic
    - Specific remedies include drugs or medication.
  - Osteopathic
    - Recognition of reciprocal interrelationship between the structure and function of the body.

Nonallopathic (Alternative Medicine)

- Chiropractors, acupuncturists, naturopaths, homeopaths
  - Five general categories
    - Alternate medical systems
    - Mind/body interventions
    - Biologically based therapy
    - Manipulative methods
    - Energy therapy

An Introduction to
Community Health Fifth Edition

Health Care Providers

- Limited care (restricted care)
  - Have advance training in a health specialty and are licensed to practice it
- Examples
  - Dentists, optometrists, podiatrists, and psychologists

An Introduction to
Community Health Fifth Edition

Nurses

- Licensed Practical Nurses (LPN)
  - 1 to 2 years of training and carry out nontechnical duties
- Registered Nurses (RN)
  - Associate or baccalaureate degree and state license
- Bachelor of Science in Nursing (BSN)
  - Prepared for additional activities involving independent judgment
- Advanced Practice Nurse (APN)

An Introduction to
Community Health Fifth Edition

Registered Nurses

Notes

Allied and Professional Health Care Providers

- Allied health care professionals
  - Provide services that assist, facilitate, and complement work of physicians
  - Nonphysician practitioners, physician assistants, dietitians, physical therapists, medical technologists, EMTs, speech therapists, and midwives
- Public health professionals
  - Work in public health clinics and voluntary agencies
  - Environmental health workers, administrators, epidemiologists, health educators, and biostatisticians

Health Care Facilities

- Practitioner offices
  Privately owned practices
- Clinics
- Hospitals
  Private
  Specialty
  Public
  Voluntary
- Ambulatory care

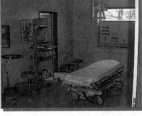

Health Care Facilities

- Rehabilitation centers
  - Long-term care options
  - Home health care
- Continuing care
  - Chronic, respite, hospice, and home care
- Accreditation

Notes

Chapter Objectives

- Identify the major concerns with the health care system in the United States.
- Explain fee-for-service and prepaid health plans.
- Briefly describe the purpose and concept of insurance.
- Define the term *insurance policy*.
- Briefly describe the State Children's Health Insurance Program (SCHIP).

Chapter Objectives

- Explain the insurance policy terms *deductible, co-insurance, co-payment, fixed indemnity, exclusion,* and *pre-existing condition*.
- Explain what is meant when a company or business is said to be self-insured.
- List the different types of medical care usually covered in a health insurance policy.

An Introduction to
Community Health Fifth Edition

Chapter Objectives

- Briefly describe Medicare, Medicaid, and Medigap insurance.
- Briefly explain long-term care health insurance.
- Define managed care.
- Define the terms *preferred provider organization* (PPO) and *exclusive provider organization* (EPO) and explain how these organizations function.

An Introduction to
Community Health Fifth Edition

Chapter Objectives

- Briefly describe the two main organizational models of health maintenance organizations (HMOs).
- Explain point-of-service, physician-hospital organizations, and Medicare Advantage.
- Identify the advantages and disadvantages of managed care.

An Introduction to
Community Health Fifth Edition

Chapter Objectives

- Identify the strengths and weaknesses of national health insurance, the Canadian health care system, and the Oregon Health Plan.
- Briefly discuss health care reform in the United States.

Introduction

- How consumers obtain health care services
- How health care services are paid and who is paying the bill
- Issues of concern
  - Access
  - Quality
  - Cost
- Potential solutions

Access and Paying for Health Care

- Every person has access to emergency medical services; however, many citizens do not have access to a primary care physician.
- 43 million American were uninsured in 2002.
- An additional 12 million did not have insurance for the full year in 2002.
- Eight of ten uninsured persons were members of working families.

Access and Paying for Health Care

- People most vulnerable to not having health insurance
  - Younger people
  - Less education
  - Lower income
  - Nonwhites
  - Not U.S. citizens
  - Males
  - Location

Notes

_____

_____

_____

_____

_____

_____

_____

_____

_____

_____

_____

_____

_____

_____

_____

_____

_____

_____

_____

_____

_____

_____

_____

_____

_____

_____

_____

_____

_____

_____

_____

_____

_____

_____

_____

_____

_____

_____

Access and Paying for Health Care

- Limited availability and accessibility of services
  - _Lack of health insurance_
  - _Inadequate insurance_
  - _Poverty_

Access and Paying for Health Care

- Medically indigent or working poor
  - Income above the poverty level
  - Poorest of the poor are usually covered by Medicaid

Access and Paying for Health Care

- Paying for health care
  - U.S. $5,440 per capita (2002)
  - More than any other nation
- Sources of payment
  - Consumers (16.6%)
  - Third-party payments
    - Private insurance companies (35.4%)
    - Public/governmental insurance (43.4%)
    - Other private funds (4.6%)

Notes

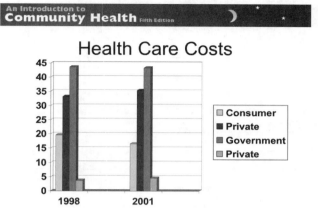

Access and Paying for Health Care

- Fee-for-service
  - The patient (first party) either pays the physician, another health care professional, or pays the facility (second party) for services rendered.
- Prepaid health care
  - Capitation system
  - Co-payments

Third-Party Payment

- Begins with health care provider
- Filing a claim

Health Insurance

- Risk and cost spreading
- System of third-party payments in which a fee for service is paid by a third party
  - An insurance company or government agency, which has collected the funds as insurance premiums or taxes
- Children's Health Insurance Program

Health Insurance Policy

- Premiums
  - Regular periodic payments.
- Deductible
  - Amount of money that the beneficiary must pay before the insurance company begins to pay for covered services.
- Co-insurance or co-payment
  - The portion or percentage of an insurance company's approved amounts for covered services that the beneficiary is responsible for paying.

Health Insurance Policy

- Fixed indemnity
  - Maximum amount an insurer will pay for a certain service.
- Exclusion
  - A specified health condition that is excluded from coverage.
- Health Insurance Portability and Accountability Act (HIPAA) of 1996
- Pre-existing condition
  - A medical condition that has been treated six months before starting a health policy.

Types of Health Insurance Coverage

- Hospitalization
  - Inpatient hospital expenses, including room, patient care, supplies, and medications
- Surgical
  - Surgeons' fees
- Regular medical
  - Nonsurgical service provided by health care providers; often has set amounts
- Long-term care
  - Array of supportive services

Types of Health Insurance Coverage

- Major medical
  - Large medical expenses usually not covered by regular medical or dental coverage.
- Dental
  - Dental procedures.
- Disability
  - Income when the insured is unable to work because of a health problem.
- Optical
  - Nonsurgical procedures to improve vision.

Trends in Insurance Coverage

- More complex plans
- Increasing diversity of products
- Delivery of care through networks
- Shifting financial structures and incentives
- Managing utilization

Cost of Health Insurance

- Cost of insurance mirrors cost of care.
- Two major factors
  - Risk of the group
  - Amount of coverage provided
- Self-insured organizations
  - Control cost of insurance

Increasing Costs of Health Care

- Due to the increasing costs, many employers are forced to do the following.
  - Increase the workers' contribution to the premium.
  - Raise the deductibles.
  - Increase the co-payments.
  - Increase the number of items on the exclusion list.

Government Health Insurance

- Medicare
  - 65 years of age and older
  - Disabled persons who are entitled to Social Security benefits
  - Administered by Health Care Financing Administration
- Part A: Hospital insurance
  - Mandatory; provided without a premium
  - Has deductible and co-insurance provisions
- Part B: Medical insurance
  - Voluntary; premium financed 75% by government
  - Has deductible and co-insurance provisions

An Introduction to
Community Health Fifth Edition

Government Health Insurance

- Controlling costs
  - Prospective pricing system
    - Diagnosis-related groups.
  - Medicare Advantage
    - Medicare managed care plan
    - Medicare private fee-for-service plan
- Medicaid
  - Policy for the poor
- Eligibility
  - Eligibility for programs is determined by each state
  - No age requirements

An Introduction to
Community Health Fifth Edition

Supplemental Health Insurance

- Medigap
  - Supplemental insurance program specifically designed for those on Medicare
  - Ten standardized plans
  - Federal government mandates a standardized policy
  - Illegal for Medicare Advantage participants
- Other supplemental insurance
  - Disease specific
  - Fixed indemnity policies
  - Long-term care insurance

An Introduction to
Community Health Fifth Edition

Managed Care

- Preferred provider organizations
- Exclusive provider organizations
- Health maintenance organizations
  - Staff model HMOs
  - Independent practice association model
- Point-of-service option
- Physician-hospital organization
- Medicare Advantage
- Medicaid and managed care

Notes

_____

_____

_____

_____

_____

_____

_____

_____

_____

_____

_____

_____

_____

_____

_____

_____

_____

_____

_____

_____

_____

_____

_____

_____

_____

_____

_____

_____

_____

_____

_____

_____

_____

_____

_____

_____

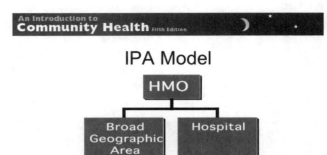

IPA Model

IPA: Individual physicians contract with an HMO to provide care for members. Providers can contract with other HMOs and/or maintain a private service. Most in the US.

Advantages and Disadvantages of Managed Care

- Benefits beyond fee-for-service system
  - Comprehensive benefits
  - Evidence-based high-quality care
  - Well-documented services
  - Integrated delivery systems
  - Accountability
- Concerns
  - Act of confidence
  - Delays in receiving care
  - Cannot understand bills
  - Believe charges are based upon coverage

National Health Insurance

- Canadian Health Care System
  - Public financed, privately delivered.
  - Each provincial and territorial authority is responsible.
  - Combination of taxes.
  - Fee for service provided; government is the only payer.
- Strengths
  - No one is without health insurance.
  - Equity across income groups.

Oregon Health Plan

- Revised Medicaid coverage
  - Addresses cost.
  - Prioritization process.
  - 709 services reduced to 587.
  - Allows every Oregonian coverage.

Chapter 15: Environmental Concerns: Wastes and Pollution

Notes

_____
_____
_____
_____
_____
_____
_____
_____
_____
_____
_____
_____
_____
_____
_____
_____
_____
_____
_____
_____
_____
_____
_____
_____
_____
_____
_____
_____
_____
_____
_____
_____
_____
_____
_____

Chapter Objectives

- Define the terms *environment, ecology,* and *biosphere*.
- Explain how human activities affect the environment through the production of wastes and residues.
- Name the primary sources of solid wastes.
- List and briefly explain the four approaches to solid waste management.

Chapter Objectives

- Define hazardous wastes.
- Explain the difference between sanitary and secured landfills.
- Identify the five approaches to hazardous waste management.
- Explain what is meant by the term *Superfund*.
- Explain the Pollution Standard Index (PSI).

An Introduction to
Community Health Fifth Edition

Chapter Objectives

- Briefly describe acid rain, the ozone layer, global warming, and photochemical smog.
- Identify the major indoor air pollutants.
- Explain the difference in point source and nonpoint source pollution.
- Identify the different types of water pollutants.

An Introduction to
Community Health Fifth Edition

Chapter Objectives

- Briefly describe the purpose of waste water treatment.
- Identify and describe two important pieces of federal legislation that protect our nation's water.
- Name the primary sources of radiation.
- Identify the pros and cons of nuclear power.
- Explain the difference between sound and noise.
- Identify approaches to reduce problems associated with noise pollution.

An Introduction to
Community Health Fifth Edition

Introduction to Environment

- External conditions, circumstances, and influences surrounding and affecting the growth and development of an organism or a community of organisms
- Ecology
- Biosphere

Notes

_____
_____
_____
_____
_____
_____
_____
_____
_____
_____
_____
_____
_____
_____
_____
_____
_____
_____
_____
_____
_____
_____
_____
_____
_____
_____
_____
_____
_____
_____
_____
_____

An Introduction to
Community Health Fifth Edition

Natural Environmental Hazards

- Natural hazards
- Biological hazards
  - Insect
  - Microbiological
  - Vegetation

An Introduction to
Community Health Fifth Edition

Natural Environmental Hazards

- Psychological hazards
  - Stress
  - Boredom
  - Anxiety
  - Fear (terrorism)
- Sociological hazards
  - Overcrowding
  - Isolation
  - War

An Introduction to
Community Health Fifth Edition

Residues and Wastes from Humans

- Contributing factors
  - Urbanization
  - Industrialization
  - Human population growth
  - Production and use of disposable products

Notes

An Introduction to
Community Health Fifth Edition

Types of Wastes and Pollution

- **Solid wastes**
- **Hazardous waste**
- **Water and its pollution**
- **Radiation**
- **Noise pollution**

An Introduction to
Community Health Fifth Edition

Solid Waste

- Sources of solid waste
  - Agriculture
  - Mining
  - Industry
  - Municipalities
  - Utilities
- Decomposing waste

An Introduction to
Community Health Fifth Edition

Sources of Waste

Notes

_____
_____
_____
_____
_____
_____
_____
_____
_____
_____
_____
_____
_____
_____
_____
_____
_____
_____
_____
_____
_____
_____
_____
_____
_____
_____
_____
_____
_____
_____
_____
_____
_____
_____
_____

Solid Waste

- Solid waste management
  - Collection
  - Transportation
  - Disposal
    - Sanitary landfills
      - Resource Conservation and Recovery Act of 1976
    - Combustion
      - Energy recovery plants
    - Recycling
      - Composition
    - Source reduction

Hazardous Waste

- Environmental Protection Agency
- A product that may
  1. Cause or contribute to an increase in mortality or to an increase in serious, irreversible, or incapacitating reversible illness.
  2. Pose a substantial present or potential hazard to human health or the environment when improperly treated, stored, transported, or disposed of, or otherwise managed.

Hazardous Waste

- Management
  - Secured landfill: least expensive
  - Deep well injection
  - Incineration of hazardous waste
  - Hazardous waste recycling and neutralization
  - Source reduction

Hazardous Waste

- **Cleanup**
- **1980: Comprehensive Environmental Response, Compensation, and Liability Act**
- **Superfund**
- **Brownfields**

Air Pollution

- Criteria pollutants
- Contaminants of outdoor air:
  - *Transportation*
  - *Electric power plants*
  - *Industry: mills and refineries*
- National Ambient Air Quality Standards
- Pollutant Standard Index

Special Concerns with Outdoor Air

- Acid rain
- Destruction of the ozone layer
  - Chlorofluorocarbons (CFCs)
- Global warming
  - Greenhouse gases
- Photochemical smog
  - Thermal inversion
  - Clean Air Act of 1963

Notes

_____

_____

_____

_____

_____

_____

_____

_____

_____

_____

_____

_____

_____

_____

_____

_____

_____

_____

_____

_____

_____

_____

_____

_____

_____

_____

_____

_____

_____

_____

_____

_____

_____

_____

_____

_____

_____

_____

_____

_____

_____

_____

An Introduction to
Community Health Fifth Edition

Indoor Air

- Indoor air pollutants
  - Asbestos
    - Biogenic pollutants
    - Combustion by-products
  - Formaldehyde
  - Radon
  - Environmental tobacco smoke
  - Volatile organic compounds

An Introduction to
Community Health Fifth Edition

Indoor Air

- Air quality and conservation
  - Sick building syndrome
  - Ventilation
  - Testing

An Introduction to
Community Health Fifth Edition

Water Pollution

- Sources of water
  - Desalinization
- Treatment of water for use
  - Coagulation and flocculation
  - Sedimentation
  - Filtration
  - Disinfection

Notes

_____

_____

_____

_____

_____

_____

_____

_____

_____

_____

_____

_____

_____

_____

_____

_____

_____

_____

_____

_____

_____

_____

_____

_____

_____

_____

_____

_____

_____

_____

_____

_____

_____

_____

_____

_____

_____

Sources of Water Pollution

- Point source pollution
  - **Single identifiable source that discharges pollutants into the water.**
- Nonpoint source pollution
  - **All pollution that occurs through the runoff, seepage, or falling of pollutants into the water.**

Types of Water Pollutants

- Biological pollutants
  - Pathogens
  - Overgrowth of aquatic plants
- Toxic pollutants
  - Inorganic chemicals
  - Radioactive materials
  - Synthetic organic chemicals

Water Quality

- Strategies to ensure safe water
  - *Water treatment*
  - *Municipal waste water treatment*
  - *Primary treatment*
  - *Secondary treatment*
  - *Tertiary treatment*
  - *Septic systems*
  - *Conservation*

Notes

_____

_____

_____

_____

_____

_____

_____

_____

_____

_____

_____

_____

_____

_____

_____

_____

_____

_____

_____

_____

_____

_____

_____

_____

_____

_____

_____

_____

_____

_____

Radiation

Sources

- Natural
  - Cosmic radiation: Sun and outer space
  - Terrestrial radiation: Earth's minerals
  - Internal radiation: Inside the body from ingestion
- Human-made
  - X-rays
  - Nuclear medicine
  - Nuclear weapons

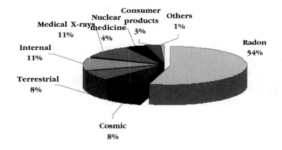

Sources of Radiation

Medical X-rays 11%
Nuclear medicine 4%
Consumer products 3%
Others 1%
Internal 11%
Radon 54%
Terrestrial 8%
Cosmic 8%

Radiation

Danger
- Roentgen equivalent man (REMS)
- Damages cells and tissues.

Policy
- U.S. Department of Energy
- Nuclear waste disposal is highly controversial.

Notes

_____

_____

_____

_____

_____

_____

_____

_____

_____

_____

An Introduction to
Community Health Fifth Edition

Noise Pollution

Measure by annoyance factor
- Amplitude
  - Decibels (dB)
- Noise abatement
  - Policy: Noise Control Act of 1972
  - Education programs
  - Environmental changes

Chapter 16: The Impact of Environment on Human Health

Notes

_____

_____

_____

_____

_____

_____

_____

_____

_____

_____

_____

_____

_____

_____

_____

_____

_____

_____

_____

_____

_____

_____

_____

_____

_____

_____

_____

_____

_____

_____

_____

_____

_____

_____

_____

Chapter Objectives

- Define the terms *environmental health* and *environmental hazard*.
- Explain the relationship between environmental sanitation, sanitary engineers, and the prevention of waterborne disease outbreaks.
- Explain the meaning of waterborne, foodborne, and vectorborne diseases and give examples of each.
- Define the term *vector* and give examples.

Chapter Objectives

- Define pest, pesticides, target organism, and persistent and nonpersistent pesticides.
- Explain the benefits and risks of using pesticides.
- Define environmental tobacco smoke, mainstream smoke, sidestream smoke, and passive smoking.
- Describe the legislation in place to deal with environmental tobacco smoke.

An Introduction to
Community Health Fifth Edition

Chapter Objectives

- Describe the sources of lead in the environment and the progress made in reducing lead levels in the United States.
- Define ionizing radiation and give examples.
- Explain the dangers of radon gas.
- Explain how human activities have increased the risk of skin cancer by altering the environment.

An Introduction to
Community Health Fifth Edition

Chapter Objectives

- Explain the relationship between psychological hazards and loss of health and give an example.
- Describe the state of population growth in the world.
- Interpret the relationship among population growth, the environment, and human health.
- Outline some solutions to population growth.
- Define natural disaster and describe two agencies involved in disaster preparedness, response, and recovery.

An Introduction to
Community Health Fifth Edition

Introduction

- Environmental health
  - Study and management of environmental conditions that affect human health.
- Environmental hazards
  - Factors or conditions in the environment that increase the risk of human injury, disease, or death.
  - Can be hazards associated with biological, chemical, physical, psychological, or sociological situations.

_____

_____

_____

_____

_____

_____

_____

_____

_____

_____

_____

_____

_____

_____

_____

_____

_____

_____

_____

_____

_____

_____

_____

_____

_____

_____

_____

_____

_____

_____

_____

_____

_____

_____

_____

_____

_____

_____

_____

_____

An Introduction to
Community Health Fifth Edition

Biological Hazards and Human Health

- Biological hazards
  - *Living organisms, or their products, that increase the risk of disease of death in humans.*
- Environmental sanitation
  - *The practice of establishing and maintaining health and hygienic conditions in the environment.*
- Sanitary engineer
  - *Protects communities from biological hazards resulting from mismanagement of waste water or solid waste.*

An Introduction to
Community Health Fifth Edition

Biological Hazards and Human Health

- Waterborne diseases
  - Poliovirus   - Amoebic dysentery
  - Hepatitis A virus - Giardiasis
  - Shigellosis   - Crytosporidiosis
  - Cholera
- Waterborne disease outbreak (WBDO)
  - Outbreaks resulting from excessive levels of the following:
    - Fluoride
    - Copper
    - Nitrites
- Spread by feces in water
  - Municipal water treatment facilities purify water
- Outbreaks still occur
- Fluoridation

An Introduction to
Community Health Fifth Edition

Biological

- Foodborne diseases
  - More than 200 diseases
  - *Salmonella*
  - *Clostridium botulinum*
- Symptoms
  - Mild to severe reactions
  - Organs involved can be the stomach, intestines, liver, kidneys, brain, and nervous system
- Foodborne disease outbreak (FBDO)
- Protection
  - Public health inspection by sanitarians
  - Hand washing
- Outbreaks of foodborne diseases

Viruses Parasites
6% 2%
Chemical
17%
Bacterial
75%

Notes

_____

_____

_____

_____

_____

_____

_____

_____

_____

_____

_____

_____

_____

_____

_____

_____

_____

_____

_____

_____

_____

_____

_____

_____

_____

_____

_____

_____

_____

_____

_____

_____

Vectorborne Diseases

- Standing water provides habitat for
  - *Pools*
  - *Tires*
  - *Open dumps*
- Zoonoses
  - *Murine typhus*
  - *Lyme disease*

Vectorborne Biological Hazards

Hazard	Agent	Vector	Disease
Virus	SLE virus	**Mosquito**	St. Louis encephalitis
	LaCrosse	**Mosquito**	LaCrosse encephalitis
Rickettsiae	R. typhi	**Flea**	Murine typhus
	R. rickettsii	**Tick**	Rocky Mt. spotted fever
Bacteria	Yersinia pestis	**Flea**	Bubonic plague
	Borrelia burg.	**Tick**	Lyme disease
Protozoa	Plasmodium sp.	**Mosquito**	Malaria
Nematodes	Wuchereria ban.	**Mosquito**	Filariasis (elephantiasis)

Chemical Hazards and Human Health

- Chemical hazards: Mismanagement of chemicals
  - *Examples*
    - Pesticides
    - Environmental tobacco smoke
    - Lead
- Pesticides
  - *Herbicides*
  - *Insecticides*

Notes

Chemical Hazards and Human Health (cont.)

- Target pest
- Target organism
- Ideal pesticide
  - *Inexpensive*
  - *Kills only target organism*
  - *Breaks down rapidly*
  - *Breaks down into harmless chemicals*

Chemical Hazards and Human Health

- Environmental tobacco smoke
  - *Sidestream smoke*
  - *Mainstream smoke*
  - *Passive smoking*
- Education
- Regulation
- Policy

Chemical Hazards and Human Health

- Lead
  - Health concerns: Anemia, birth defects, bone damage, neurological damage, kidney damage
  - Chronic in nature
  - Children at greatest risk
  - Sources: Gasoline, water pipes, and drinking water tainted by lead leached from landfills

Notes

Lead (cont.)

- Comprehensive Environmental Response, Compensation, and Liability Act (CERCLA)
- This act allowed the CDC to provide grants to allow states to do the following:
  - Screen infants and children for elevated lead levels.
  - Ensure referral for medical and environmental intervention.
  - Provide education to parents and children about lead poisoning.

Physical Hazards and Human Health

- **Radon contamination**
  - **Natural element found in most rock and soils**
  - **Lung cancer**
  - **Enters buildings through the following:**
    - **Cracks in the foundation walls and floors**
    - **Joints**
    - **Openings around sump pump drains**
    - **Loose-fitting pipes**
    - **Porous building materials**

Physical Hazards and Human Health

- **Ultraviolet radiation**
  - **Sunshine wavelengths**
  - **Destruction of the ozone layer**
  - **Skin cancer**

Notes

_____

Psychological Hazards and Human Health

- **Difficult to define and measure**
- **Many mental states associated**
- **Intentional terrorism**

Sociological Hazards and Human Health

- **Often combined with other environmental hazards.**
- **Population growth demonstrates sociological hazards.**

Population Growth

- Population growth attributed to
  - Birth rate
  - Death rate
  - Migration
- Principles
  - Lag phase
  - Exponential phase
  - Equilibrium phase

Notes

Population Growth: S-Curve

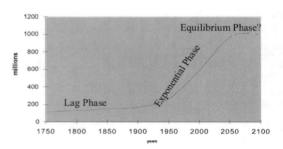

Population Growth

- Issues
  - Global warming
  - Acid rain
  - Depletion of the ozone
  - Increasing crime rates
  - Epidemics
- Solutions
  - Various methods of conception control
  - Birth control methods
  - Social policies

Site and Location Hazards and Human Health

- Natural disasters
  - *Geophysical and meteorological events*
  - *Involves interaction of disaster agents*
  - *Magnitude of overall loss*
  - *Increase in biological, psychological, and sociological hazards*

- Primary needs after a disaster
  - *Food*
  - *Water*
  - *Shelter*
  - *Health care*
  - *Clothing*
- Federal Emergency Response Agency (FEMA)

Notes

_____

_____

_____

_____

_____

_____

_____

_____

_____

_____

_____

_____

Natural Disasters

- Emergency support functions (federal agencies)
  - Transportation (DOT)
  - Communications (NCS)
  - Construction (DOD)
  - Firefighting (DOA)
  - Damage information (FEMA)
  - Mass care (ARC)
  - Department of Homeland Security
  - Health & medical (DHHS & PHS)
  - Resources support (GSA)
  - Urban search & rescue
  - Hazardous materials (EPA)
  - Food (DOA)
  - Energy (DOE)
  - Stand-by disaster agents

Notes

Chapter Objectives

- Describe the importance of injuries as a community health problem.
- Explain why the terms *accidents* and *safety* have been replaced by the currently more acceptable terms *unintentional injuries, injury prevention,* and *injury control* when dealing with such occurrences.
- Briefly explain the difference between intentional and unintentional injuries and provide examples of each.

Chapter Objectives

- List the four elements usually included in the definition of the term *unintentional injury*.
- Summarize the epidemiology of unintentional injuries.
- List strategies for the prevention and control of unintentional injuries.
- Explain how education, regulation, automatic protection, and litigation can reduce the number and seriousness of unintentional injuries

Chapter Objectives

- Define the term *intentional injuries* and provide examples of behavior that results in intentional injuries.
- Describe the scope of intentional injuries as a community health problem in the United States.
- List some contributing factors to domestic violence and some strategies for reducing it.

Chapter Objectives

- List some of the contributing factors to the increase in violence related to youth gangs and explain what communities can do to reduce this level of violence.
- Discuss intervention approaches in preventing or controlling intentional injuries.

Definitions

- Injury
  - Acute exposure to physical agents interacting with the body in amounts or at rates that exceed the threshold of human tolerance.
- Unintentional injuries
  - Injuries judged to have occurred without anyone intending harm to be done.
- Intentional injuries
  - Injuries that have been purposely inflicted, whether by oneself or another.

Notes

An Introduction to
Community Health Fifth Edition

Characteristics of Unintentional Injuries

1. Unplanned events
2. Preceded by an unsafe act or condition
3. Accompanied by economic loss
4. Interrupt the efficient completion of tasks

An Introduction to
Community Health Fifth Edition

Cost of Injuries to Society

- 5.8 million death per year worldwide
- 157,078 deaths per year in the United States
  - 101,537 (64.6%) unintentional
  - 30,622 (19.5%) suicides
  - 20,308 (12.9%) homicides
  - 4,241 (0.03%) undetermined intent
- 50.5 million injuries
- 20 million disabling injuries
- $586 billion/year on unintentional injuries

An Introduction to
Community Health Fifth Edition

Causes of Years of Potential Life Lost (YPLL) (per 100,000 pop.)

Notes

_____
_____
_____
_____
_____
_____
_____
_____
_____
_____
_____
_____
_____
_____
_____
_____
_____
_____
_____
_____
_____
_____
_____
_____
_____
_____
_____
_____
_____
_____
_____
_____
_____
_____
_____
_____

Cost Estimate (billions 1999 U.S. dollars)

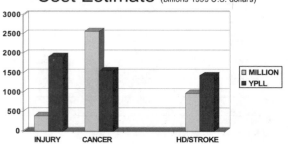

Legend:
- □ MILLION
- ■ YPLL

Categories: INJURY, CANCER, HD/STROKE

Unintentional Injuries

- Motor vehicle crashes
  - Number 1 cause of unintentional injury deaths
  - 42,815 fatalities in 1999
  - 2.9 million nonfatal injuries in 1999
- Other types
  - Falls: 15,764 deaths
  - Suffocation: 5,555 deaths
  - Poisonings: 14,078 deaths
  - Fires and burns: 3,309 deaths
  - Drowning: 3,281 deaths
  - Discharge of firearms: 802 deaths

Epidemiology of Unintentional Injuries

- Person
- Age
  - Leading cause of death in the 1- to 44-year age group.
- Gender
  - Males are twice as likely to be affected as females.
- Minority status
  - Leading cause of death for all racial and ethnic groups except blacks

Notes

_____

_____

_____

_____

_____

_____

_____

_____

_____

_____

_____

_____

_____

_____

_____

_____

_____

_____

_____

_____

_____

_____

_____

_____

_____

_____

_____

_____

_____

_____

_____

_____

_____

_____

_____

_____

_____

_____

Epidemiology
of Unintentional Injuries

- Place
  - Home
    - More unintentional injuries occur in the home than in any other place.
  - Highway
    - Ranks second for nonfatal injuries; ranks first for unintentional injury deaths.
  - Recreation/sports area
    - Third mostly likely place to sustain injury.
  - Workplace
    - Fourth highest rate of unintentional injuries.

Unintentional Deaths Location
(US 1999)

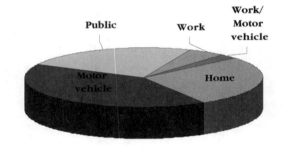

Epidemiology
of Unintentional Injuries

- Time
  - Motor vehicle crashes
    - Highest rate in November and December.
    - More fatalities occur on Fridays through Sundays.
    - Alcohol is involved in half of fatal crashes.
  - Drowning
    - More occur in the summer months.
    - Alcohol is involved in nearly half.
  - Fires
    - More occur in the winter months.

Prevention Through Epidemiology

- Injury Prevention and Control Contributors
  - Hugh De Haven
  - John E. Gordon
  - William Haddon, Jr.
- Public Health Model
  - Similar to communicable disease model except agent is "energy" in this model.

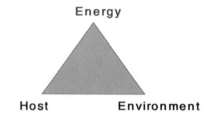

Public Health Model for Unintentional Injuries

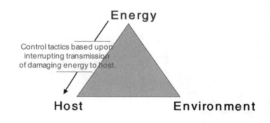

Public Health Model for Unintentional Injuries

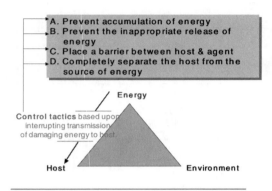

Public Health Model for Unintentional Injuries

The figure contains:

A. Prevent accumulation of energy
B. Prevent the inappropriate release of energy
C. Place a barrier between host & agent
D. Completely separate the host from the source of energy

Control tactics based upon interrupting transmission of damaging energy to host.

Energy

Host   Environment

An Introduction to
Community Health Fifth Edition

Community Approach to Prevention of Unintentional Injuries

- Education
- Regulations
- Emergency response system
- Automatic protection
- Litigation

An Introduction to
Community Health Fifth Edition

Injuries

- Intentional
  - Approximately 50,000 people die each year.
  - Approximately 5.7 million receive nonfatal injuries as a result of interpersonal violence.
- Types
  - Assaults
  - Family violence
  - Rape
  - Robbery
  - Suicide
  - Homicide

Notes

_____

_____

_____

_____

_____

_____

_____

_____

_____

_____

_____

_____

_____

_____

_____

_____

_____

_____

_____

_____

_____

_____

_____

_____

_____

_____

_____

_____

_____

_____

_____

_____

_____

_____

_____

_____

_____

_____

_____

An Introduction to
Community Health Fifth Edition

Epidemiology
of Intentional Injuries

- Rates of homicide, assault, and rape
  - Homicide rate 5.5 per 100,000.
  - Declining rates.
  - Risk factors.
- Suicide and attempted suicide
  - Nearly 30,000 suicides are reported each year.
  - Rates among the young have tripled since 1950.
- Firearm injuries
  - Second leading cause of injury death.
  - 38% of homicide and 57% of suicides involved a firearm.

An Introduction to
Community Health Fifth Edition

Violence in Our Society

- Individuals and violence
  - Lack communication and problem-solving skills.
  - Firearms are easy to obtain and deadly.
- Family violence and abuse
  - 1 in 6 homicides is the result of family violence.
  - Child maltreatment
    - Child abuse
    - Child neglect
    - Intimate partner violence
- Model for abuse
- Gangs and violence

An Introduction to
Community Health Fifth Edition

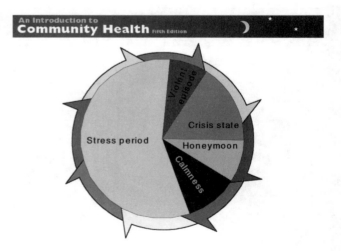

Approaches to Prevention

- Education
  - Safe School/Healthy Student Initiative
- Employment and recreation opportunities
- Regulation and enforcement
  - Brady Bill
  - Electronic detection of weapons
  - Other types of regulation
- Counseling and treatment
  - Represent secondary and tertiary prevention

Chapter 18: Safety and Health in the Workplace

Notes

Chapter Objectives

- Describe the scope of the occupational safety and health problem in the United States and its importance to the community.
- Identify some of the pioneers in the prevention of occupational injuries and disease.
- Provide a short history of state and federal legislation on occupational safety and health.

Chapter Objectives

- Explain the difference between occupational injuries and occupational diseases and give several examples of each.
- Discuss the types of injuries that frequently occur in the workplace and describe their occurrence with regard to person, place, and time.
- Briefly describe broad strategies for preventing injuries in the workplace.

Chapter Objectives

- Identify the different types of occupational illnesses and disorders and list some of the causative agents.
- Outline some general strategies for controlling these diseases.
- List several occupational safety and health professions and describe what the professionals in each of these do.
- List and briefly describe several occupational safety and health programs for the workplace.

Introduction

- 2.6 billion workers
- 250 million occupational injuries
- 330,000 fatalities
- 1.1 million worker deaths each year from work-related illnesses
- 160 million new cases of diseases resulting from the worker's environment

Definitions

- Occupational disease
  - An abnormal condition, other than an occupational injury, caused by an exposure to environmental factors associated with employment.
- Occupational injury
  - An injury that results from exposure to a single incident in the work environment.

Notes

_____

_____

_____

_____

_____

_____

_____

_____

_____

_____

_____

_____

_____

_____

_____

_____

_____

_____

_____

_____

_____

_____

_____

_____

_____

_____

_____

_____

_____

_____

_____

_____

_____

_____

_____

Occupational Injuries, Diseases, and Deaths

- Scope of the problem
  - Estimated cost of $146.6 billion annually.
  - $74 billion in lost wages and productivity.
  - $27.7 billion in medical costs.
  - $26.3 billion in administrative costs.
  - 15 die each day from work-related injuries.
- Impact is beyond the workplace.

History of Occupational Safety and Health Problems

- 1561: _De Re Metallica_
- Industrial Revolution
- State legislation
  - Workers' compensation laws
- Federal legislation
  - Occupational Safety and Health Act of 1970
  - National Institute for Occupational Safety and Health (NIOSH)

Highlights of Federal Occupational
Safety and Health Legislation

Year	Legislation
1908	Federal Workmen's Compensation Act (limited coverage)
1916	Federal Highway Aid Act
1926	Federal Workmen's Compensation Act (included workers)
1927	Federal Longshoremen's & Harbor Workers' Compensation Act
1936	Walsh-Healey Public Contracts Act
1952	**Coal Mine Safety Act**
1959	Radiation Standards Act
1960	Federal Hazardous Substances Labeling Act
1966	National Traffic & Motor Vehicle Safety Act
	Child Protection Act (banned hazardous household substances)
1967	National Commission on Product Safety created
1968	Natural Gas Pipeline Safety Act
1969	Construction Safety Act
	Coal Mine Health & Safety Act
1970	**Occupational Safety & Health Act**

Notes

Prevalence of Occupational Injuries, Disease, and Deaths

- Recent trends
  - Since 1992, the numbers of injuries and illnesses have declined.
  - Goods-producing sector has the highest incidence.
  - Workplace injury and illness rates cycle up and down.

Unintentional Injuries

- Fatal work-related injuries
  - 15 fatal work-related injuries per day.
- Nonfatal work-related injuries
  - 3.5 million occupational injuries and illnesses were treated in emergency rooms in 2001.
- Characteristics
  - Age
    - Injuries lowest for 16- to 19-year age group.
    - Death rates highest for 65+-year age group.
  - Gender
    - Males at a higher risk of injury.
  - Poverty and race

Workplace Fatalities (1999)

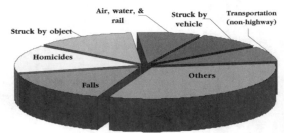

Notes

Unintentional Injuries

- Geographic differences
  - Alaska and Wyoming are the states with the highest rates.

- Temporal variations
  - 81% decline in deaths from injuries between 1912 and 2002.

Workplace Injuries by Industry and Occupation

- Fatal injuries by industry
  - Mining
  - Agriculture
  - Construction
  - Transportation
- Nonfatal occupational injuries
  - Goods-producing sector
  - Service-producing sector

Prevention and Control of Unintentional Injuries in the Workplace

- Reduction of injuries by:
  - Eliminating or modifying the job
  - Changing the work environment
  - Making machinery safer
  - Improving the selection, training, and education of workers

Notes

_____

_____

_____

_____

_____

_____

_____

_____

_____

_____

_____

_____

_____

_____

_____

_____

_____

_____

_____

_____

_____

_____

_____

_____

_____

_____

_____

_____

_____

_____

_____

_____

_____

_____

_____

_____

_____

_____

_____

_____

_____

Workplace Violence

- Categories
  - Criminal intent
  - Customer/client
  - Worker-on-worker
  - Personal relationship
- Risk factors
  - Location
  - Time
  - Type of work

Workplace Violence

- Prevention strategies
  - Environmental design
    - Separate workers
    - Better lighting
    - Security system
  - Administrative controls
    - Policies
    - Procedures
  - Behavior strategies
    - Training

Occupational Illnesses and Disorders

- Musculoskeletal conditions
  - Repeated trauma
- Skin disease and disorders
  - Allergic and irritant dermatitis
- Noise-induced hearing loss
- Respiratory disorders
  - Chronic nature
  - Difficult to recognize
- Other work-related diseases and disorders
  - Poisoning and infections
  - Anxiety, stress, or neurotic disorders

Prevention and Control of Occupational Diseases and Disorders

- Agent-host-environment model
  - Identification and evaluation of agents
  - Procedures
  - Engineering controls
  - Protective devices
  - Surveillance

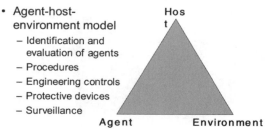

Host

Agent   Environment

Resources for Prevention

Safety and health professionals
- Safety engineers and certified safety professionals
- Health physicists
- Industrial hygienists
- Occupational physicians
- Occupational health nurse

Resources for Prevention

Occupational Safety and Health Programs
- Preplacement examinations
- Disease prevention programs
- Safety programs
- Health promotion programs
- Employee assistance programs